Workbook and Awareness Journal

By
Michelle May, M.D.

Am I Hungry?

PUBLISHING

Phoenix, Arizona

Am I Hungry? Workbook and Awareness Journal

ISBN 10 1-934076-13-9
ISBN 13 978-1-934076-13-2

Michelle May, M.D.
P.O. Box 93686
Phoenix, AZ 85070-3686

IMPORTANT NOTICE: PLEASE READ

In view of the complex, individual nature of health and fitness issues, this book, and the ideas, programs, procedures, and suggestions are not intended to replace the advice of trained medical professionals. All matters regarding one's health require medical supervision.

The author's role is strictly educational in the context of this workshop and materials. The author is not providing any medical assessment, individualized therapeutic interventions or personal medical advice. Seek medical advice from your personal health care provider regarding your personal risks and benefits insofar as adopting the recommendations of this program.

The author disclaims any liability arising directly or indirectly from the use of this book or program.

Dedicated to all of my workshop participants
- you taught me so much!

TABLE OF CONTENTS

Workshop 1 – In Charge, Not In Control

Think: Why Do I Eat? 11

Live: Increase Your Metabolism 20

Eat: Fuel Your Metabolism 23

Awareness Journal 25

Workshop 2 – Trust Your Gut Instincts

Think: Am I Hungry? 33

Live: Born to Move 38

Eat: All Foods Fit 42

Awareness Journal 45

Workshop 3 – It's Not About the Food

Think: I'm Not Hungry – What Now? 53

Live: Change Your Mind 61

Eat: Drink and Be Merry 64

Awareness Journal 67

Workshop 4 – Head Hunger

Think: What Am I Really Hungry For? 75

Live: One Step at a Time 94

Eat: Clearing Carb Confusion 98

Awareness Journal 109

Workshop 5 – Goodbye Guilt

Think: What Do I Eat? 117

Live: Stretch Yourself 123

Eat: Fat Facts 126

Awareness Journal 135

Workshop 6 – Mindful Eating

Think: How Do I Eat? 143

Live: Be Strong 147

Eat: Protein Power 150

Awareness Journal 157

Workshop 7 – Just Right

Think: How Much Do I Need? 165

Live: In Motion 170

Eat: Nutrition at a Glance 175

Awareness Journal 179

Workshop 8 – Self-Care Buffer Zone

Think: Where Do I Invest My Energy? 187

Live and Eat: A Flexible Approach to Self-Care 195

Awareness Journal 201

WELCOME

This workshop will guide you through a whole new way of managing your weight.

○ You'll learn how to be in charge of your eating instead of feeling out of control.

○ You'll learn how to eat the foods you love without overeating—and without guilt.

○ You'll learn how to increase your metabolism.

○ You'll learn how to eat healthier foods without depriving or restricting yourself.

Weight management is actually quite simple. It boils down to energy balance: calories in vs. calories out. The problem of course is that many people are out of balance. They consume too many convenient, high fat, high-calorie foods and beverages and live relatively sedentary lifestyles. Although we'll cover fitness and nutrition, our focus will always be on *why* you do what you do in the first place.

USING THIS WORKBOOK

This Workbook and Awareness Journal will give you brief summaries of each workshop along with questions to help you apply the concepts to your own life. Each chapter will cover three important sections:

Think – This is all about *why* and *how* we make decisions. When you change the way you think, you change the way you feel, which changes the way you act which leads to changes in your results.

Live – This section is about your activity. After all, one of the main reasons you need to eat is to fuel living. We'll talk about how to increase your metabolism, how to increase your physical activity level and exercise, improve your health and live a fulfilling life.

Eat – This section focuses on your food choices. You probably already know a lot about nutrition if you've done any dieting, but we'll try to clear up the confusion without giving you a bunch of rules to follow. Also enjoy great recipes to practice what you learn.

WORKSHOP NOTES

THINK: WHY DO I EAT?

Self-Awareness Quiz

Rate the following statements on a scale of 1 to 10 with 1 = "I completely DISAGREE with this statement" and 10 = "I completely AGREE with this statement." Write your answers in column #1 after the first workshop and column #2 after the last workshop.

#1	#2	
5	1	I am hungry all the time.
1	1	I am never hungry.
8	3	I can't tell when I'm hungry.
10	6	I know I'm not hungry but I eat anyway.
1	1	I am starving by the time I eat, so I'll eat anything I can get my hands on.
5	7	I eat by the clock.
8	3	I think about food all of the time.
7	1	I love food and eating too much to be a healthy weight.
7	2	I think healthy food is boring.
10	6	I use food to cope with stress and other feelings.
10	7	I am an emotional eater.
10	4	I eat when I'm bored.
10	6	I eat when I'm stressed.
10	1	I eat when I'm nervous.
10	2	I eat when I'm sad.
10	4	I eat when I'm angry.
10	2	I eat when I'm lonely.
10	7	I eat when I'm tired.
8	2	I reward myself with food.
10	5	I comfort myself by eating.

6	3	I celebrate every special occasion or milestone by eating.
8	2	I don't know why I eat.
10	1	I often eat until I am stuffed.
10	4	I have trouble stopping myself when I eat "bad" foods.
6	7	I have tried a lot of diets.
8	2	I am either dieting or eating too much.
8	8	I don't have enough willpower to stick to a diet.
8	2	I think thin people have more willpower than I do.
8	3	I think thin people have better metabolisms than I do.
8	4	I feel guilty about eating certain foods.
5	1	I have a love-hate relationship with food.
3	1	I sometimes ignore hunger in order to control my weight.
6	3	I eat on a schedule (i.e. six times a day) even when I'm not hungry.
2	5	I decide ahead of time what I'm going to eat for the entire day.
7	5	I avoid certain foods because they are fattening.
6	2	I am confused about what I should be eating.
3	1	I am frustrated that the "experts" keep changing what we should eat.
5	5	I hate to exercise.
3	1	I don't really like exercise but I do it so I can eat what I want.
1	1	I exercise extra if I eat too much.
6	1	I dread the thought of going on another diet but I don't know what else to do.

Look back over your ratings. The statements that you rated a 5 or higher are probably the issues that you'll need to work on throughout this program. What are they? Any aha's?

You'll take this Self-Awareness Quiz again when you have completed this program in order to see what has changed.

EATING STYLES AND EATING CYCLES

? Describe someone you know who manages their weight effortlessly.

INSTINCTIVE EATING

How some people are able to manage their weight effortlessly:

- They eat when they're hungry (they just know when their body needs food).
- They stop when they're satisfied (even if there's food left on their plate).
- They eat whatever they want (hopefully making healthy choices).
- They live an active lifestyle (this may or may not involve regular exercise).

The 'classic' example of Instinctive Eating is a baby. Children are born with the ability to know exactly when and how much to eat. The good news is that we all started out this way. To better understand why they do what they do, look at their Eating Cycle.

THE EATING CYCLE

The Eating Cycle is a way to understand the decisions you make when you eat.

WHY? Why do I eat? This is the major underlying purpose or motivation driving the eating cycle. In other words, what is your "cycle driver" at any given time?

WHEN? When do I want to eat? When do you feel like eating? What causes an urge to eat?

WHAT? What will I eat? What food do you choose to eat from all the possible options?

How? **How do I eat?** How does food get from the plate or container into your body?

How Much? **How much do I eat?** How much fuel do you give your body?

Where? **Where do I invest my energy?** Once you have chosen and eaten food to fuel your body, where do you invest that energy (including your physical, emotional, mental and spiritual energy).

THE INSTINCTIVE EATING CYCLE

Let's apply the Eating Cycle to Instinctive Eating.

Why? The purpose of eating is to respond to hunger to nourish and fuel your body.

When? You eat when the physical signs of true hunger strike and the food you are hungry for is available. You just *know* you need to eat.

What? You choose the food you're hungry for or what you think is best and most satisfying from what is available. You may be conscious of nutrition and other factors when making your food choice.

How? You eat with the intention of satisfying hunger so you're likely to be attentive to your food. You are more likely to eat calmly, slowly and without distraction.

How Much? You eat until you're comfortably satisfied; that may mean going back for seconds or leaving some on your plate.

Where? Energy goes to work, play and exercise. Your physical energy can be directed towards your activities; your emotional energy can be focused on your relationships and feelings; your mental energy can be focused on daily tasks and goals; your spiritual energy can be used for seeking peace, joy and purpose. Once the fuel is depleted or stored, the symptoms of hunger develop and the cycle repeats itself.

? Describe someone you know who struggles with their weight and overeating.

OVEREATING

(handwritten: Visual, stay awake, fatigue)

Why some people struggle with eating and weight:

- They often eat due to external and emotional triggers.
- They are often food focused.
- They often eat to excess.
- They may view exercise as punishment for overeating.

THE OVEREATING CYCLE

WHY? The cycle drivers are triggers (i.e. to satisfy some other need). Eating provides *temporary* pleasure or distraction.

WHEN? Have an urge to eat due to physical, environmental and emotional triggers.

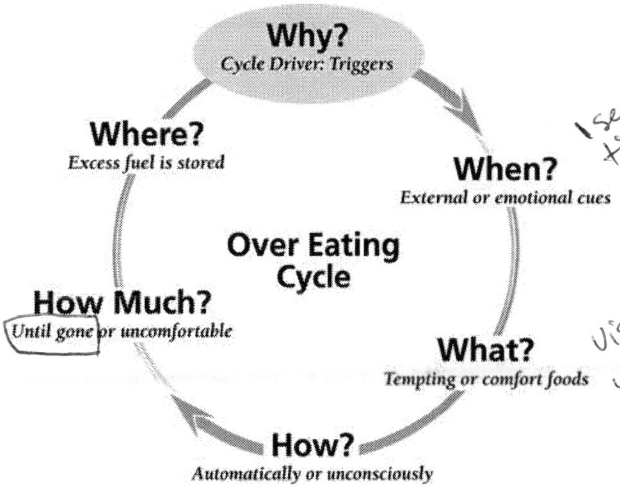

Eat in response to *physical* triggers other than hunger:

- Thirst
- Fatigue
- Pain

Eat in response to *environmental* triggers:

- Seeing or smelling food
- Advertising, cooking shows, recipes
- Seeing other people eating
- Time of day or year (mealtimes, holidays, seasonal)

Why?
Cycle Driver: Triggers

Where?
Excess fuel is stored

When?
External or emotional cues

Over Eating Cycle

How Much?
Until gone or uncomfortable

What?
Tempting or comfort foods

How?
Automatically or unconsciously

(handwritten: I see food, tired)

(handwritten: Visual – what's available)

○ Popcorn at the movies or doughnuts in the break room

○ Food left on a plate, like their children's unfinished lunch

Eat in response to *emotional* triggers:

○ Stress

○ Comfort

○ Lonely

○ Sad

○ Bored

○ Frustrated

○ Angry

○ Even happy emotions like celebration, love and reward

WHAT? The food choice is driven by the trigger.

Write the foods you associate with each of the triggers above.

How? How do people eat in an Overeating Cycle?

○ Fast, "speed-eating." Leads to less satisfaction and more eating

○ Distracted, doing something else (working, watching TV, driving or reading).

○ Alone, in secret. Results in guilt which drives the Overeating Cycle

How Much? Since hunger didn't tell you to eat, what will tell you to stop?

○ Food is gone

○ Bag or container is empty

○ TV show, movie or other activity is over

○ Someone comes home or something else interrupts your eating

○ Feeling miserably full, "stuffed," or physically sick

○ Feeling numb

WHERE? Where does the energy go? Your body stores the extra fuel. You may feel more sluggish and be less active.

? Describe someone you know who manages their weight by dieting.

RESTRICTIVE EATING

How some people manage their weight:

○ They are preoccupied with food and their weight.

○ They see food as good or bad.

○ See themselves as good or bad depending on what they ate or what they weigh.

○ They may exercise rigidly to earn food or punish themselves for eating.

THE RESTRICTIVE EATING CYCLE

WHY? Your cycle is driven by the rules – the expert's rules or your own rules.

WHEN? The "rules" of your current diet tell you when to eat (i.e. 6 small meals per day, nothing after 6 pm).

WHAT? This is what most diets focus on. You eat what the "rules" of the current diet tell you to eat (i.e. no carbs, low fat etc.). This may be based on calories, grams, exchanges, points or other ways of limiting your intake. You may also be influenced by your morning weight or how well you followed your diet the day before.

Why?
Cycle Driver: Rules

Where?
Spent on diet and exercise

When?
According to the rules

Restrictive Eating Cycle

How Much?
Allowed amount

What?
"Good" or allowed foods

How?
Rigidly

How? Food is prepared and consumed in a controlled, rigid manner. You have to weigh, measure and count your food and write it down to keep track.

HOW MUCH? This is determined by how much the rules allow, such as one ounce of cheese, 12 grapes, four grams of carbs.

WHERE? Sticking to a diet requires a lot of mental, emotional and sometimes physical energy. Exercise may be used to earn the right to eat or pay penance for eating something "bad." If you significantly under-eat on a regular basis, your body will attempt to conserve energy by lowering your metabolism.

CYCLE SWITCHING

The Restrictive Eating Cycle is not sustainable in real life for most people. Stressors and triggers may overwhelm the dieter, usually leading to the end of the diet. When the diet ends, your exercise program usually does too. Many people switch between the Restrictive and Overeating Cycles. We call this Cycle Switching, also known as yo-yo dieting. There may be days, months or even years between cycles or you can switch back and forth within the same meal.

Many people vibrate in a constant state between Restrictive Eating and Overeating. When they're being "good" they feel deprived; when they're eating what they want they feel guilty.

? Would you describe your "eating style" as mostly Overeating, Restrictive Eating or Instinctive Eating? The following questions will help you decide:

Why do you eat? *triggers, meal times, fatigue*

When do you feel like eating? *When do I not?,*

What do you eat? *High calorie, high fat foods, starting to shift this a bit.*
(oatmeal, almonds)

How do you eat? *mindlessly*

How much do you eat? *until food is gone, I don't like to have leftovers.*

Where do you spend your energy? *Don't spend it all – I store it.*

? Do you switch back and forth between Overeating and Restrictive Eating (Cycle Switching)? How does this affect your eating and your weight?

very long overeating cycles between restrictive eating

The way to break this frustrating pattern is to relearn to eat according to your Instinctive Eating Cycle. You'll learn the strategies for each step in the Instinctive Eating Cycle throughout the following seven chapters.

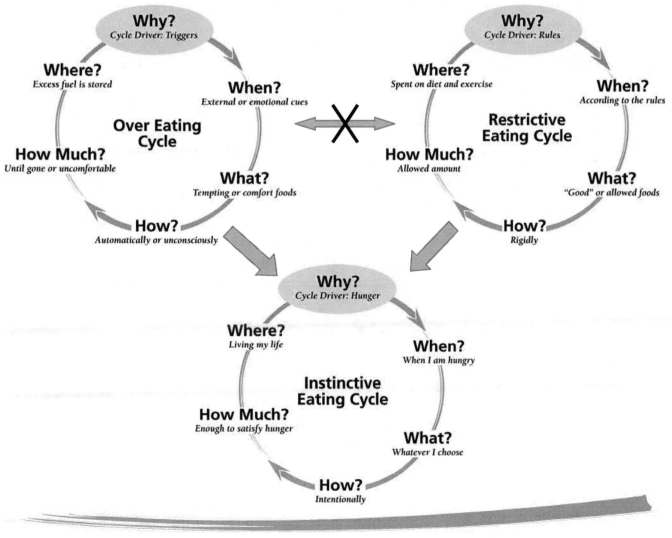

LIVE: INCREASE YOUR METABOLISM

You hear the word "metabolism" tossed around all the time, but what is it and why is it important? Metabolism refers to the amount of fuel (energy), measured in calories, that your body burns each day.

? Do you think your metabolism is low, average or high? Why?

Low – Hashimoto's (hypothyroidism).

Your basal metabolism is the number of calories your body burns to support basic, vital daily functions like your heart beat and breathing. All *activity* (from brushing your teeth to running a marathon) burns calories above your basal metabolism. Regular *exercise* causes a significant boost in metabolism. You burn calories during the activity and sometimes for several hours *after* the activity.

Increasing your *muscle mass* with strength training will also boost your metabolism. On the other hand, a loss of muscle mass (a common result of dieting and decreased activity with aging) will decrease your metabolism so you burn fewer calories each day.

? What will you do this week to increase your metabolism?

Walk 20-30 mins/day. Find my weights + start using them every other day.

Start using your metabolism to your advantage by increasing your physical activity and increasing your muscle mass. You'll learn more in the following chapters but beginning right now, take charge of your health.

YOUR PERSONALIZED EXERCISE PRESCRIPTION

If you could bottle exercise, you would have the closest thing there is to a wonder drug. Since you can't get it in a pill, you'll have to put in a little more time and effort, but look at what it can do for you!

Brand Name: Exercise

Generic Names (Numerous effective generics available): aerobics, basketball, bike riding, body sculpting, dancing, hiking, housework, playing with children, racquetball, rowing, stretching, swimming, tennis, walking, weight lifting, working out, yard work, yoga and many others.

Indications: Shown to be very effective for weight management and relief of fatigue, stress, low self-esteem, insomnia, boredom, and symptoms of depression and anxiety. May prevent, improve, or delay the onset of the following conditions: overweight and obesity, diabetes, high blood pressure, high cholesterol, heart disease, some types of cancer, some forms of arthritis, fibromyalgia, PMS, constipation, addictions and many other health problems.

Benefits: Increased energy and productivity, increased metabolism, weight loss, improved sense of well-being and appearance, better sleep patterns, improved appetite regulation, lower blood sugar, lower heart rate and blood pressure, higher HDL ("good") cholesterol, improved blood sugar control, and reduced risk of cancer.

Side Effects: Patients report feeling stronger, healthier, and more youthful.

Precautions: You should consult with your physician first, especially if you have any chronic medical conditions or unexplained symptoms. If you develop unexpected shortness of breath, chest, jaw, neck, or arm pain or pressure, rapid or irregular heart rate, lightheadedness, pain, or any other unexplained symptoms, stop and seek immediate medical advice and attention.

Dosage: Start with small doses taken most days of the week and increase gradually as tolerance develops. Dosage may be adjusted as needed to accommodate other responsibilities. However, due to the many beneficial effects, consistent usage is highly recommended. Choose from the numerous generic brands available. Alternate brands as needed to improve overall level of fitness, maintain interest and assure compliance.

WARNING: Likely to become habit-forming when used regularly!

WRITE YOUR OWN EXERCISE PRESCRIPTION

One of the most powerful steps you can take, whether you want to improve your diet, your physical activity or any other aspect of your life, is to write down your goals and the specific steps you are going to take to achieve them. When you write down your goals, you are creating instructions for your subconscious mind to carry out.

Practice goal setting by writing your own exercise prescription. Write down the specifics: what type of activity(ies) you will do, when, how often, how long and how much effort you will use.

Am I Hungry? Exercise Prescription

NAME_____ DATE_____

REFILL **FREQUENTLY!** SIGNED _____

 EAT: FUEL YOUR METABOLISM

There is another way to improve your metabolism – by fueling it. Starvation (literal or self-imposed through dieting) causes a decrease in your metabolism. This is because your body has a basic survival mechanism. When the food supply is adequate, you consume and burn fuel as needed. When the food supply is decreased (i.e. famine), your body shifts into starvation mode which lowers your metabolism and uses muscle mass as fuel (lowering metabolism even further).

Today most famines are self-imposed diets. If you lose "weight" on a restrictive diet, what do you lose? You lose fat, water (especially the first week and especially with low carb diets) and muscle. When the diet is over, if you regain your weight, what do you get back? Fat. You don't get your muscle back unless you exercise. This results in a higher body fat percentage and a lower metabolism. This is less healthy and makes it even easier to gain weight.

Have you ever gained more weight after a diet than you lost? This is the result of rebound overeating (making up for feeling deprived) and a decrease in your metabolism.

Do you think your metabolism has been affected by your eating patterns? How?

In order to reverse this process, you'll learn how to pay attention to hunger to guide your eating in the next chapter.

ACTION PLAN

○ Set aside 15-30 minutes each day for reading, journaling and thinking about what you are learning. This is an important practice for this process – and for your life.

○ Use Chapter 1 of your *Awareness Journal* to write down your observations and insights.

○ Notice why you are eating and see if you can determine which Eating Cycle you are in at any given time.

○ Notice when you feel like eating, what you feel like eating, how you eat, how much you eat and where you spend your energy. What patterns, triggers and cycle drivers do you recognize?

YOUR GOALS FOR THE WEEK

Awareness Journal		
Date / Time	Food and Drink Type and Approximate Amount	Notes
Physical Activity		What I did to boost my metabolism

Food for Thought

At what point will society begin to doubt the wisdom of the diets rather than the fortitude of the dieters?

Awareness Journal		
Date Time	Food and Drink Type and Approximate Amount	Notes
Physical Activity		What I did to boost my metabolism

Food for Thought

*Instead of following strict rules created by "experts,"
you can become the expert on meeting your needs.*

\multicolumn{3}{c}{**Awareness Journal**}		
Date **Time**	**Food and Drink** Type and Approximate Amount	**Notes**
Physical Activity		**What I did to boost my metabolism**

Food for Thought

The sensations of hunger and satiety are the simplest, yet most powerful tools available to you for reconnecting with your instinctive ability to know what your body needs.

Awareness Journal		
Date Time	Food and Drink Type and Approximate Amount	Notes
Physical Activity	**What I did to boost my metabolism**	

Food for Thought

Imagine what it will be like when you re-establish physical hunger as your primary cue for eating and learn to satisfy your other needs in positive and constructive ways. You will create new pathways for eating and for living.

\	Awareness Journal	
Date **Time**	**Food and Drink** Type and Approximate Amount	**Notes**
Physical Activity		**What I did to boost my metabolism**

Food for Thought

Instead of focusing on what and how much food you should eat, the key is first understanding why you want to eat in the first place. This awareness will give you the opportunity to meet your true needs appropriately.

        www.AmIHungry.com

Awareness Journal		
Date Time	Food and Drink Type and Approximate Amount	Notes
Physical Activity		**What I did to boost my metabolism**

Food for Thought

By focusing on hunger as your guide, you'll become your own internal expert for when, what, and how much to eat. You don't have to be in control, but you'll learn to be in charge.

Awareness Journal		
Date Time	Food and Drink Type and Approximate Amount	Notes
Physical Activity		What I did to boost my metabolism

Food for Thought

Step by step, you will learn a whole new way to manage your weight and build optimal health. You will free yourself from your focus on food and weight and discover new tools and energy to lead a more fulfilling, balanced life.

WORKSHOP NOTES

THINK: AM I HUNGRY?

In the last chapter we explored the *Why* of the Eating Cycle. In Instinctive Eating the *why* is hunger; in Overeating the *why* is triggers, in Restrictive Eating the *why* is rules. Now, let's turn our focus to *When*.

Hunger is a basic survival mechanism. The purpose of hunger is to signal your brain that your body needs nourishment and energy. You were born with the ability to know when you need fuel. Many people who struggle with their weight are disconnected from their signals of hunger and satisfaction.

Am I hungry? This deceptively simple question can be the answer to ending your struggle with weight and food—without dieting. It is so important that the only "rule" we ask you to follow is: whenever you have an urge to eat, first ask yourself, "Am I hungry?"

What Isn't Hunger?

? What other things besides hunger might trigger you to want to eat? How could you deal with those instead of eating?

Opportunity - availability of food. Just seeing it. I often eat something because its there - things I wouldn't have eaten if I'd had never been there. Sweets at work, for example.

I feel like I go "unconscious" just before I eat it - to bypass that mechanism that would make me stop & question if I was really hungry.

This was an emotional week - finding out about Wayne. I'm sure I over-ate in response

There are numerous triggers for eating that we'll cover in detail in the next two chapters. For now, here is a quick look at other triggers and ways to deal with them:

○ Thirst. Try drinking a glass of water instead.

○ Fatigue. Eating will make you feel more tired. Rest or take a nap instead.

○ Salivation - typical response to sight, smell, and sometimes thought of food. Wait for other physical symptoms of hunger.

○ Urge to chew, suck or crunch something. Chew gum or suck on ice.

○ Cravings. Cravings can be triggered by food you saw, thought of, have been missing or associate with certain feelings or events. There is no problem with eating something you're craving—but wait until you're hungry.

○ Environment – what you're doing, who you're with or something you saw. Distract yourself until you're actually hungry.

○ Boredom. Eating is certainly something to do, but could you find something else to do until you get hungry?

○ Tension or stress. Food only works temporarily. Try relaxation techniques instead.

○ Emotions – sad, mad, glad, etc. Much more on this in the next two chapters.

The purpose of asking yourself, "Am I hungry?" before you eat is to tune into whether your *need* to eat or *want* to eat.

? How can you tell when you are hungry? Write down all the signs that your body needs fuel.

stomach growls
irritability
distractibility

Am having trouble distinguishing between true hunger and the anxiety I get if it's "time" to eat and I'm not sure. I felt a "pressure" in my stomach but couldn't tell if it was really hunger.

SIGNS OF HUNGER

- Hunger Pangs or gnawing
- Growling
- Emptiness
- Nausea
- Irritability
- Headache
- Low energy/fatigue
- Difficulty concentrating
- Feeling you must eat now

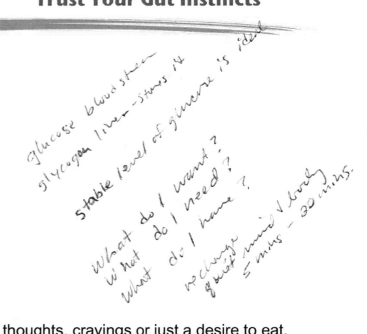

The signs of hunger are physical. They are not thoughts, cravings or just a desire to eat.

STRATEGIES: IDENTIFYING HUNGER

Whenever you feel like eating the first thing you need to do is ask yourself, "Am I hungry?" Here are some strategies to help you answer this question accurately.

- **Move away from the food.** This will allow you to focus, calm yourself and pay attention to what your body is telling you. Go to a "food-free" zone that you don't associate with eating. At a restaurant, determine whether you're hungry before you go inside. At a party or other social gathering, go outside or to the bathroom. If you can't escape the food, close your eyes or turn away from it and focus inward.

- **Focus on your physical sensations.** Take a couple of deep breaths to calm yourself and focus on your physical sensations. Ask yourself: "How does my stomach feel?" Put your fist there or picture it as a balloon. Is it empty, full or in-between? Notice other sensations. Are you light-headed, queasy or irritable?

- **Focus on your thoughts and feelings.** Are you thinking something like, "Better eat while I have a chance," "It's been a few hours since I ate," or "Mmmm, that looks delicious – and it's free!" Remember, hunger is a physical feeling, not a thought.

Feeling anxious, sad, lonely, angry or even happy can also trigger an urge to eat, but that is not the same thing as hunger.

HOW HUNGRY AM I?

As you become used to recognizing hunger, you'll see that there are different levels of hunger. They will help you decide when to start eating and when to stop. Use the Hunger & Fullness Scale to identify your hunger levels before, during and after eating. The scale is not intended to set strict guidelines about when you should eat but rather, to help you develop awareness of your body's own signals.

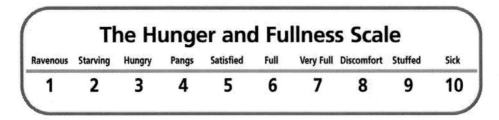

The Hunger and Fullness Scale

Ravenous	Starving	Hungry	Pangs	Satisfied	Full	Very Full	Discomfort	Stuffed	Sick
1	2	3	4	5	6	7	8	9	10

Here are some descriptions to help you learn what the numbers mean:

1 **Ravenous:** Too hungry to care what you eat. This is a high risk time for overeating.

2 **Starving:** You feel you must eat NOW!

3 **Hungry:** Eating would be pleasurable but you could wait longer.

4 **Hunger pangs:** You're slightly hungry; you notice your first thoughts of food.

5 **Satisfied:** You're content and comfortable. You're not hungry or full - you can't feel your stomach at all.

6 **Full:** You can feel the food in your stomach.

7 **Very full:** Your stomach feels stretched and you feel sleepy and sluggish.

8 **Uncomfortable:** Your stomach is too full and you wish you hadn't eaten so much.

9 **Stuffed:** Your clothes feel very tight and you're very uncomfortable.

10 **Sick:** You feel sick and/or you're in pain.

? How do you feel physically and emotionally and what happens when…

… you are a 5 or above when you start to eat?

Feel out of control

… you are a 4 when you start to eat?

… you are a 2 or 3 when you start to eat?

Rarely a 2 or 3

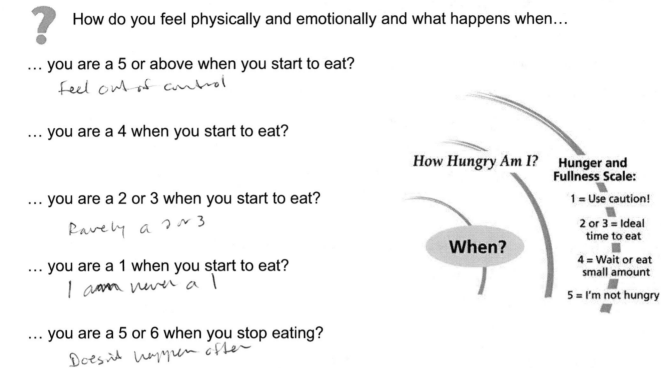

How Hungry Am I? **Hunger and Fullness Scale:**

1 = Use caution!

2 or 3 = Ideal time to eat

When?

4 = Wait or eat small amount

5 = I'm not hungry

… you are a 1 when you start to eat?

I am never a 1

… you are a 5 or 6 when you stop eating?

Doesn't happen often

… you are a 7 or higher when you stop eating?

Feel gross— tell myself "remember this feeling" but never do

HUNGER RHYTHMS

Now that you know the basics of hunger, there are other factors that can help you understand and use your personal hunger rhythms.

○ It may take 20 to 30 minutes after eating to tell you are full.
○ Hunger cannot be satisfied before it occurs. That is called preventive eating.
○ Hunger can be postponed until it is more convenient to eat.
○ Hunger doesn't follow a clock, but you can "train" yourself to be hungry at certain times.
○ Eating small meals satisfies hunger best and reassures your metabolism.
○ Hunger is affected by what you eat and how much you eat.
○ Hunger may be specific for a certain type of food.

LIVE: BORN TO MOVE

Movement is instinctive and but modern society has developed ways to do almost everything more efficiently, automatically and effortlessly. While these conveniences may save time, they also save energy – your energy, which may result in weight gain. Even more significantly, less movement and a low level of physical activity results in decreased fitness so you may not have the stamina, strength or flexibility to live your life to the fullest.

? Think about your lifestyle. Are you active or ~~sedentary~~? Do you avoid doing things that require effort? Are you able to comfortably do all of the things you would like?

yes - send Skype upstairs for things   *No!*

When most people think of 'getting active' they immediately have visions of treadmills and aerobic classes and have negative thoughts and feelings about it. In truth, there are many ways to increase your physical activity, improve your physical fitness and boost your metabolism without creating a rigid exercise program that you don't enjoy.

? What specific things can you do to increase your physical activity in the following areas of your life?

○ Leisure   *go for walks, actively play ō Skype at playground, play Twister*

○ Home   *Do more housework!*

○ Work   *use weights while I'm at my desk*

○ Out doing errands   *park farther away from entrances*

○ Travel

GET FITT

On the following page you'll read about using a pedometer to measure your lifestyle activity and motivate yourself to be come more physically active. As you become more active in your daily life, your body will adapt and gradually become more physically fit. This will allow you to further increase your physical activity and even begin a more structured program in order to improve your level of fitness.

The FITT principle will help you create a program that is just right for you, no matter where you are starting from. **FITT** stands for:

Frequency: How often you do the activity

Intensity: How much effort you use during the activity

Time: How long you do the activity

Type: What kind of activity you choose

Measure your baseline activity using a pedometer. Then use FITT to evaluate and develop your personal fitness plan and adjust it gradually to get the best results.

? What specific things will you do this week to increase your lifestyle activity?

? If you are ready to start exercising or are already exercising, write down your plan for the week using FITT. (If you have any health problems or unusual symptoms, be sure to get clearance from your doctor to exercise.)

As you practice looking for ways to become more physically active, it will become automatic. Instead of thinking, "I don't have time to exercise," or "I don't like exercise," think, "I am a fit and active person." This thought will lead you to look for opportunities to prove yourself right. You'll see the stairs instead of the elevator, you'll carry in your own groceries, you'll look forward to making the bed and you'll invite your friend for a walk or a game of tennis instead of lunch.

USING A PEDOMETER TO INCREASE YOUR ACTIVITY

A pedometer is a fun way to measure your activity level throughout the day, both during routine activities and while exercising. It is a small device that is worn on your waist to measure the number of steps you take or the distance you walk, making it easy to set realistic goals for yourself. It is really motivating to see those steps add up—and see your energy level rise as your fitness improves.

Why Use a Pedometer?

Numerous studies have shown that activity level is one of the most important determinants of successful weight loss and maintenance, as well as overall good health. Increased activity throughout the day ("lifestyle fitness") and setting aside the time for several weekly sessions of exercising makes all the difference.

How Do You Use a Pedometer?

Wear your pedometer on your waist, attached to your belt, skirt or pants (even your underclothes as long as it fits snugly against your body.) Place it in line with the seam of your slacks or over the center of your kneecap, parallel to the ground. It will not give accurate readings if it is tilted to one side. Try it out in different positions along the waist; count the number of steps you take and compare that to what the pedometer actually reads.

Put your pedometer on when you first get up and wear it all day long. At the end of the day, record the number of steps you took then press the reset button to return the step counts back to "0" for the next day.

Increasing Your Steps

Get an idea of your baseline activity level by recording the number of steps you take without changing your normal routine. Once you know your baseline, set specific goals for increasing the number of steps you take each day or week.

Watch the steps add up when you pace while you talk on the phone, walk a flight of stairs, skip a half hour TV program and walk the dog (add about 2000 steps!), walk instead of drive, park further, or window shop with friends instead of sitting to talk. Of course not all activities can be counted in steps (for example, swimming or yoga) but they still count toward your fitness.

Use the following chart to track your progress. You'll find that using a pedometer for simple, accurate feedback will motivate you to take a step in the right direction!

TRACKING MY STEPS

Start Date _____ Starting average step count _____ I will increase by _____ steps each week

Step Count

	Monday	Tuesday	Wednesday	Thursday	Friday	Saturday	Sunday	Average
Week 1								
Week 2								
Week 3								
Week 4								
Week 5								
Week 6								
Week 7								
Week 8								

Am I Hungry?

EAT: ALL FOODS FIT

Labeling foods "good" or "bad" is one of the many habits we've picked up from dieting.

? Make lists of foods that you think of as:

Good	Bad
fruits, veggies	Anything with trans fats
whole grains	Anything with high
lean meats	fructose corn syrup
nuts + seeds	Anything with artificial
milk	sweetners

? Look at the foods on your lists. Why did you label each food in this manner? Are you certain that these labels are completely accurate? Why or why not?

The bad foods are detrimental to your health + the good foods have life sustaining nutrients

? When you eat a food from the "bad list," how do you feel? What happens?

For sometimes I don't think about it, other times I feel bad that I'm hurting myself.

Labeling and attempting to avoid particular foods can lead to feelings of deprivation, increased cravings and, ultimately, overeating these "forbidden foods." This usually increases guilt, frustration and feelings of hopelessness while your weight increases. When you place food on a pedestal you actually give that food *more* power over you.

Definitions of good and bad are determined by the latest expert, the most recent study, the last diet book or even what the celebrities are eating. There isn't always agreement on the definition of "good" and "bad" foods, leading to confusion about what to eat

We have found it far more effective to use an "all foods fit" approach. In other words, instead of placing certain foods on a pedestal, all foods are on an even playing field. When you are free to choose from all foods, you're less likely to overeat certain foods simply because you feel you have broken the rules. You are back in charge. With an "all foods fit" foundation you can use the following three principles to answer ANY questions you have about what to eat!

Balance: Be flexible with your food choices to balance your intake of food from all of the food groups. It is also important to balance eating for health with eating for pleasure.

Variety: Focus on eating a variety of different foods to increase your nutrient intake, prevent monotony and increase enjoyment.

Moderation: Moderation is eating just enough. You have the instinctive ability to know that eating just sweets for example, is not moderation.

Do you eat a balance and variety of food in moderation? What specific steps will you take to increase the balance, variety and moderation in your diet this week?

No. Shop c a grocery list to ensure variety.

 **ACTION PLAN**

○ Set aside 15-30 minutes each day for reading, journaling and reflecting on this process.

○ Use Chapter 2 of your *Awareness Journal* to write down your observations and insights.

○ Before you eat, ask yourself, "Am I hungry?" and practice identifying the physical signs of hunger.

○ Give yourself a "Hunger and Fullness" number before, during and after eating.

○ Begin to identify where those other urges to eat are coming from.

○ Become more active every day.

○ Start or continue an exercise program using FITT.

○ Use the principles of balance, variety and moderation to guide eating.

YOUR GOALS FOR THE WEEK

Awareness Journal

Date Sun 12/16 Time	Food and Fluids Type and Approximate Amt.	Physical Symptoms, Thoughts and Feelings	How Hungry Am I? Before Eating	How Hungry Am I? After Eating
1:00pm	ham + cheese sandwich, clementine orange	slight headache, slight gurgling	2	6
	1 cup coffee c̄ 1% milk	really needed the caffeine		
	1 more cup coffee/milk	full but wanted the coff - I always need more than 1 cup	1-2	4
5:30	small handful almonds	felt like I really needed to eat		
6:00	eggs (2 yolks) 1½ slices toast, cauliflower c̄ cheesy sauce	didn't really feel well - low grade headache	3	5-6
10:30	100 calorie bag popcorn + diet Coke	stomach was bothering me - hunger?	4	5

Lifestyle Activities	Physical Activity Notes: FITT
laundry, XMAS tree, cleaning	very active today

Food for Thought

You can relearn to trust your body to let you know if and when you need food and how much you need to eat.

Awareness Journal

Date 12/8/09 Tues Time	Food and Fluids Type and Approximate Amt.	Physical Symptoms, Thoughts and Feelings	How Hungry Am I?	
			Before Eating	After Eating
6:40	corn bread	not really hungry but felt I need to eat	4	6
	2 large cups coffee	needed to wake up		
10:30	small handful almonds	stressed	5	5
12:00	granola bar	stressed	3-4	4-5
1:30	ham/cheese sandwich	tired	3-4	6
	clementine orange			
	Diet Coke	↓		
6:30	steak		3	6
	cauliflower & cheese			
	ice cream drumstick			
9:30	ice cream drumstick		5	6
1:00 am	bowl cheerios / milk	tired	5	6

Lifestyle Activities	Physical Activity Notes: FITT
walking	

Food for Thought

Whenever you want to eat ask yourself, "Am I hungry?" This important question will help you recognize the difference between an urge to eat caused by the physical need for food, from an urge to eat caused by other triggers.

Awareness Journal				
Date Time	Food and Fluids Type and Approximate Amt.	Physical Symptoms, Thoughts and Feelings	How Hungry Am I?	
			Before Eating	After Eating

Lifestyle Activities	Physical Activity Notes: FITT

Food for Thought

When you wait until you are hungry, eating is more pleasurable and satisfying. Hunger is truly the best seasoning!

Awareness Journal

Date Time	Food and Fluids Type and Approximate Amt.	Physical Symptoms, Thoughts and Feelings	How Hungry Am I?	
			Before Eating	After Eating

Lifestyle Activities	Physical Activity Notes: FITT

Food for Thought

If you aren't hungry when you start eating, how do you know when to stop?

	Awareness Journal			
Date **Time**	**Food and Fluids** Type and Approximate Amt.	**Physical Symptoms, Thoughts and Feelings**	**How Hungry Am I?**	
			Before Eating	After Eating

Lifestyle Activities	Physical Activity Notes: FITT

Food for Thought

Since your stomach is about the size of your fist, it only takes
a palm-full of food to fill it. When you don't overfill your stomach,
you will feel light and comfortable after eating.

Awareness Journal				
Date Time	Food and Fluids Type and Approximate Amt.	Physical Symptoms, Thoughts and Feelings	How Hungry Am I?	
			Before Eating	After Eating

Lifestyle Activities	Physical Activity Notes: FITT

Food for Thought
When you eat food your body didn't ask for,
it has no choice but to store it.

Awareness Journal				
Date Time	Food and Fluids Type and Approximate Amt.	Physical Symptoms, Thoughts and Feelings	How Hungry Am I?	
			Before Eating	After Eating

Lifestyle Activities	Physical Activity Notes: FITT

Food for Thought

When you are hungry, instead of turning to a long list of restricted and allowed foods, keep in mind that all foods fit! Use the principles of Balance, Variety, and Moderation to guide your choices.

WORKSHOP NOTES

THINK: I'M NOT HUNGRY - WHAT NOW?

The only "rule" is: Whenever you have an urge to eat, ask yourself, "Am I hungry?" Why isn't the rule, "If you aren't hungry, don't eat"?

When you recognize that an urge to eat is not from physical hunger, what are your choices?

Regret vs. guilt

YOU HAVE THREE CHOICES

Eat Anyway – Yes, this *is* an option! Even people who eat instinctively sometimes eat when they aren't hungry. Remember you're in charge. If eating isn't an option, then you're in a Restrictive Eating Cycle, leading to more eating.

Distract Yourself – Find something to do until the urge passes or hunger comes.

Meet Your True Needs – Figure out why you want to eat and do something to meet that need instead. We'll use a strategy called FEAST which is an acronym for Focus, Explore, Accept, Strategize and Take Action; more on that later.

CHOICE 1: EAT ANYWAY

When you're in charge, you make decisions with full awareness. What are the advantages and disadvantages of eating anyway when you aren't hungry?

Advantages

○ Easy - no effort, thought or energy because you've done it many times before.

○ Temporary pleasure – for example, reward or celebration.

○ Temporary distraction – for example, postpone something or avoid or distract yourself from a feeling.

Disadvantages

○ Discomfort – both physical (stuffed) and emotional (regret). Note: regret is different from guilt; no need to feel guilt if you made a conscious choice to "eat anyway." Guilt would just lead to more overeating.

○ Weight gain – When you eat food your body didn't tell you to, it has to store it.

○ Unmet Needs – When you meet your needs with food, you're not truly meeting your needs. When your true needs are unmet, your triggers will return again and again.

CHOICE 2: DISTRACT YOURSELF

 What are the advantages and disadvantages of distracting yourself when you aren't hungry?

Advantages

○ Urge to eat will likely pass

○ More productive use of time than eating.

○ Disrupts your Overeating Cycle.

○ Especially useful for environmental triggers.

○ You'll get to eat when you're hungry and then it will be more satisfying.

Disadvantages

❍ Requires some thought and effort.

❍ Requires some preparation.

❍ Temporary – fine if there was an environmental trigger that will pass anyway.

❍ May not meet your true needs.

STRATEGIES: DISTRACTING YOURSELF

❍ Make a list of distraction activities (see 101 Things to Do Besides Eat).

❍ Choose activities that are enjoyable, like a new hobby.

❍ Strive to find activities that revitalize, relax or nurture you.

❍ Choose activities that are "eating incompatible" – you can't eat while you do them.

❍ Have some activities that are simple and quick and some that are more time consuming so you'll have activities for a variety of situations.

❍ Promise yourself that you'll try distraction for at least at little while e.g. 15 minutes.

❍ Be prepared with things to do and have the necessary supplies on hand.

❍ Create a Distraction Kit with the things you need to distract yourself like stationary, craft supplies, an inspirational book, your journal, cards, etc.

❍ Establish a Food Free Zone at home and at work.

❍ Create "rules" for yourself if they are helpful.

In the following table, list a variety of distraction activities under each heading. When you're finished, go back through your lists and put a number by each activity indicating the following: 1 = Sounds great

2 = Sounds good

3 = Tolerable

Cross off any activities that aren't at least tolerable. Strive to have plenty of "1"s and some "2"s, and fewer "3"s. If your choice was between eating or doing something you dread, what would you be most likely to choose? Also, make a note by activities that are good for certain situations, i.e. while you are at work.

Simple/Quick	Complex/Time Consuming
1 Call a friend (home/work)	2 Organize a closet (home)

Distraction is not a punishment; you're not distracting yourself to deprive yourself. The goal is to distract yourself until you're actually hungry. Distraction is most effective when the trigger is boredom, an environmental trigger or when you aren't able to figure out or meet your true needs. If you always choose to distract yourself and never address the underlying trigger, it will continue to cause an urge to eat. Which brings us to your third option:

CHOICE 3: MEET YOUR TRUE NEEDS

What are the advantages and disadvantages of meeting your true needs when you want to eat but you're not hungry?

Advantages

- ❍ Decreases triggers - Discovering what is triggering the urge to eat and addressing the underlying need will eventually cause that trigger to decrease significantly.
- ❍ When food is no longer used to meet needs, you may lose weight or, at a minimum, have more success at weight maintenance.
- ❍ When your true needs are recognized and met, you move toward optimal health.
- ❍ Leads to the best long term results.
- ❍ The process will also help you learn how to deal with other issues in your life.

Disadvantages

○ Most challenging (but also the most rewarding!)

○ Requires time, effort and energy.

○ Requires openness and honesty with self and often with others.

○ May require the assistance of others to work through issues and develop new skills.

When a craving doesn't come from hunger, eating will never satisfy it. When you don't meet your true needs, those unmet needs can actually drive your Overeating Cycle. Clearly, this is the most effective option (though not always the easiest).

Struggling with overeating doesn't mean that you have a dark, deep psychological issue. It often means that you have learned to cope with certain situations or emotions in certain ways. But at least you've been coping.

However, sometimes there is an underlying issue that needs to be dealt with. Examples include symptoms of depression, anxiety or an eating disorder or other problems that indicate a need for additional help so seek the advice of a health care professional. There is effective treatment available.

FEAST

Using the acronym FEAST, there are five steps you can take that will help you become aware of *why* you experienced the urge to eat and take small steps toward meeting that need. **FEAST** stands for **F**ocus, **E**xplore, **A**ccept, **S**trategize, **T**ake Action.

F = Focus

The first step is to focus and tune into your body, your thoughts and your feelings without judgment. Start with a Mind-Body Scan:

○ **Focus your attention inward.** Move away from food, close your eyes and take a few deep breaths.

O **Focus on your physical state.** Are you hungry or full? What is your hunger number? Do you notice any particular areas of your body? Are there any areas of discomfort or does your body feel good?

O **Focus on your thoughts.** What is going through your mind? Don't worry about what the thoughts are; just observe them.

O **Focus on your feelings.** What emotions are you aware of? Is there any sadness, anger, guilt, fear or happiness? Complete the sentence: I feel _____ or I am _____. Feelings can usually be described in a word or two whereas thoughts are sentences or phrases.

? What are some other ideas for ways you can get in touch with what you are thinking and feeling?

Suggestions: Journal, talk it through with a friend or counselor, draw or scribble, notice if the cravings give you clues, imagine someone helping you like a parent or a trusted friend. Maybe there is a part of you who does this well for other people but not yourself, for example the way you parent your children or manage your employees that you can tap into to help yourself.

E = EXPLORE

Once you're aware of your physical sensations, thoughts and feelings, you can begin to explore them—again without judgment. Your triggers can be just about anything physical, environmental or emotional. Some are just learned habits like eating popcorn at the movies. Others triggers are more significant, like an attempt to cope or meet important needs and may take a little more exploration. We'll explore common triggers and strategies for dealing with them in the next workshop.

A = ACCEPT

Be nurturing and supportive toward yourself. It's alright to feel the way you do. There is no need for thoughts of right or wrong, bad or good, should or shouldn't have. Even though eating hasn't been the most effective way for you to cope in the past, that doesn't mean you should feel guilty or ashamed. At least you've been coping in some way. Now you have the awareness and the opportunity to choose a more effective way. You'll probably feel more calm and able to cope after this step.

S = STRATEGIZE

Be a problem solver; come up with as many creative solutions as you can to address the trigger. Examples: Develop a hobby, make new friends, talk to a friend or co-worker, buy a book on the subject, discuss your concerns with the person directly or see a counselor. Don't worry about making the right choice; just come up with new strategies and make adjustments until you figure out what works for you.

T = TAKE ACTION

This is about being in charge. Take a step in the direction you wish to go – no matter how small the step seems.

Though it is more challenging to go through the steps outlines in FEAST, you'll get the best long term results. You'll learn to recognize your true needs and meet them more effectively. You may be surprised at how quickly your urge to eat diminishes and how much better you feel overall.

101 THINGS TO DO BESIDES EAT

When you recognize that an urge to eat was caused by a trigger rather than true hunger, you can choose to do another activity to distract yourself until the urge passes. Highlight the ideas that appeal to you and add some of your own. Remember, try to choose activities that are enjoyable, available and preferably, eating incompatible. Create a "Distraction Kit" or drawer with everything you need to distract yourself. Establish a Food Free Zone in your home or office that is perfect for these moments.

Imagine a healthier, energetic you * Walk around the block * Call a friend * Make a list of your Top Ten Reasons to get active * Read a child a book * Make a To Do list * Dance a little * Plan a vacation * Get a massage * Jot a thank you note to someone * Go to bed early * Read a great book * Write in your Awareness Journal * Give yourself a manicure or pedicure * Plan a healthy meal for your family * Surf the Internet * Finish an unfinished project * Walk your dog * Feel your feelings * Volunteer in your community * Start a hobby * Brush your teeth * Tape your favorite show to watch while exercising * Take 5 slow, deep cleansing breaths * Practice an instrument * Balance your checkbook * Plan a party * Say a prayer * Buy yourself some flowers * Do a few sit-ups * Make a phone call to someone you like * Chop veggies to keep on hand * Set your priorities * Try a new hairstyle * Give a massage * Write down something you are proud of this week * Clean out a junk drawer * Play a game with your kids * Try a new route on your walk * Scream! * Plant fresh herbs to use in your cooking * Drink a glass of water * Kiss someone * Try on some of your clothes * Catch up on your reading for work * Look at old pictures * Rent a video * Smell the roses * Wash your car * Chew some gum * Plan a "date" for someone special * Swim a few laps * Read Am I Hungry? * Take a hot, soothing bath * Update your calendar * Get it off your chest * Build something * Check in on an elderly person * Work in your yard * Start your holiday shopping list * Count your blessings * Write a letter * Fold some laundry * Listen to your inner conversations * Take a nap * Run an errand * Work on your budget * Take a bike ride * Check your e-mail * Make a positive statement about yourself - repeat often * Give your dog a bath * Start a project you've been wanting to get around to * Send a birthday card * Meditate * Try a healthy new recipe * Play cards * Set your goals * Freshen your make-up * Hug someone * Rearrange some furniture * Go take a hike! * Help with homework * Light a fire or some candles * Say "STOP!" out loud * Put your pictures in an album * Walk around your workplace * Try a new relaxation technique * Talk it over with someone * Get a head start on your taxes * S-t-r-e-t-c-h * Do a "Honey Do" * Say what's on your mind * Go pick up your mail * Straighten a closet * Think * Do something nice for someone anonymously * Check the stock market * Plan a romantic encounter * Clean out a files * Tell someone how you really feel * When you become truly physically hungry, eat!

LIVE: CHANGE YOUR MIND

? Are you doing regular physical activity? If not, what does your "little voice" say that keeps you from doing it?

I'm tired!,
I'm exhausted

Do you have negative thoughts about physical activity and about yourself like "hate," "should," "lazy?" Your words and thoughts are so powerful that your brain will seek evidence to prove that they are accurate. For example, when you say "I'm lazy," you'll behave in a way that supports that definition of yourself so you'll end up proving yourself right. That is because your thoughts lead to your feelings which lead to your actions which lead to your results:

Thoughts > Feelings > Actions > Results

The goal then is to develop more effective thoughts that will lead to the results you want. Furthermore, your brain can only comprehend what it already believes to be true. For example, if you think you have to go to a gym to exercise, you'll walk right by the stairs and stand in front of the elevator because your brain doesn't see the stairs as an opportunity.

When you're struggling with physical activity or other lifestyle choices, see what your little voice is saying. Then, pretend you are talking to your best friend or a child. Use supportive, encouraging words and creative suggestions.

Take a look at the following chart of common mind games that people play. See if you can begin to think in a more positive way in order to get yourself more active.

I don't have time
- You have time to do what is most important to you
- Being active and fit makes you more productive
- How much time do you spend on activities that don't really provide any benefits (TV, surfing the internet, talking on the phone, being inefficient, etc.)?

I have too much to do
- Move exercise up on the priority list
- Schedule your exercise as an appointment
- Be consistent but flexible

I'm too tired
- Consistent exercise boosts energy levels and promotes better sleep
- Do several short bouts spread throughout the day
- Exercise in the morning
- Promise yourself you'll do at least ten minutes. If you're still tired, try again tomorrow.

I don't enjoy it
- Where does this "dread" come from?
- Negative thoughts about exercise often come from old information (embarrassment, pain, punishment for eating) that doesn't need to apply anymore.
- Try a new or different activity.

I'm embarrassed
- No one is really looking at you anyway; they're too focused on themselves

It's too hard (or It's too uncomfortable or I'm not athletic)
- Start slowly and build very gradually
- Create small rewards for small steps

What thoughts do you have about being physically active? What feelings, actions and results do those thoughts cause?

Your thoughts are so powerful! If you repeat the mantra "I am a fit and active person" over and over, your brain will actually look for opportunities to make that so. You'll see the stairs instead of the elevator and you'll park at the first spot you see rather than driving around and around. You'll gradually become a fit and active person.

What could happen if you began to think of yourself as a fit and active person?

EAT: DRINK AND BE MERRY

You won't get a list of rules to follow about what to eat so you'll get to make your own choices. That means you'll need to know about your options and how they affect your body.

There are six major classes of nutrients: water, carbohydrates, protein, fat, vitamins and minerals. They provide different functions in the body. Let's start with water.

About 60-70% of your body is water. Water helps with blood flow, digestion, transporting nutrients and regulating body temperature. Because these are important, your body works hard to maintain proper fluid balance – and works very hard if you don't drink enough. Many people live in a state of mild dehydration and they don't even know it. They may experience fatigue and lack of stamina. When you don't drink enough water, your body will begin to store extra fluid in your tissues. Once you start drinking enough, your body will release that extra fluid. Imagine being able to get rid of extra fluid and boost your energy level just by increasing your fluid intake.

HOW MUCH FLUID DO YOU NEED?

Rule of thumb = 8 to 12 8-oz. glasses per day.

Better indicator = the color of your urine. When you are well hydrated your urine will be "dilute" and will appear pale colored. (Supplements and medications can darken urine).

GETTING THE MOST FROM FLUIDS

Balance

- ○ Keep water handy. You will not drink it if it is not easily accessible.
- ○ Be aware of salt, caffeine and alcohol which can affect your fluid balance.
- ○ Drink more during exercise, warm weather and illness.

Variety

- Although plain water may not be appealing to you at first, you'll develop a taste for it.
- Eventually you'll find that water really satisfies your thirst best.
- Most people enjoy their water better when it is cold.
- Spice it up with a splash of lemon, lime, cranberry juice, cucumber or mint.
- You can also get fluid from foods like soups, salads, fruits and vegetables. And having a bowl of clear broth soup at the beginning of a meal has been shown to decrease calorie intake during that meal.

Moderation

- Moderation – What "foods" are you drinking? Many liquids like juice, smoothies and coffee drinks have as many calories as a serving of food--or an entire meal!
- Determine if drinking satisfies your hunger as well as eating actual food. For example, you might find that having a glass of water and an orange is more satisfying than a glass of orange juice.

? What specific things will you do this week to improve the quantity and quality of fluid that you drink?

 **ACTION PLAN**

○ Set aside 15-30 minutes each day for reading, journaling and reflecting on this process.

○ Use Chapter 3 of your *Awareness Journal* to write down your observations and insights.

○ Make your list of "Things to Do Besides Eat" and create a Distraction Kit to keep all of your supplies handy.

○ Establish a Food Free Zone in your home and at work.

○ Identify at least one need that has been triggering your overeating and take specifics steps for meeting that need more effectively using FEAST.

○ Listen to see what your little voice is saying about physical activity and begin to replace those thoughts with more effective thoughts.

○ Work on improving the amount and type of fluids you drink.

YOUR GOALS FOR THE WEEK

Awareness Journal

Date Time	Food and Fluids Type and Approximate Amt.	Physical Symptoms, Thoughts and Feelings	How Hungry Am I?	
			Before Eating	After Eating

Thoughts about Exercise	Physical Activity Notes: FITT

Food for Thought

It is not necessary to make a perfect choice every time in order to break free from overeating. It is more a matter of becoming aware, recognizing that you have choices and taking small steps toward meeting your true needs.

Awareness Journal				
Date Time	Food and Fluids Type and Approximate Amt.	Physical Symptoms, Thoughts and Feelings	How Hungry Am I?	
			Before Eating	After Eating

Thoughts about Exercise	Physical Activity Notes: FITT

Food for Thought

Your thoughts lead to your feelings, which lead to your actions, which lead to your results. If you don't like your results, ask yourself what you were thinking first.

Awareness Journal				
Date Time	Food and Fluids Type and Approximate Amt.	Physical Symptoms, Thoughts and Feelings	How Hungry Am I?	
			Before Eating	After Eating

Thoughts about Exercise	Physical Activity Notes: FITT

Food for Thought

When a craving doesn't come from hunger,
eating will never satisfy it.

Awareness Journal				
Date Time	Food and Fluids Type and Approximate Amt.	Physical Symptoms, Thoughts and Feelings	How Hungry Am I?	
			Before Eating	After Eating

Thoughts about Exercise	Physical Activity Notes: FITT

Food for Thought

Don't wait for the perfect time to begin exercising. It is unlikely that the perfect time will ever come—and it won't last forever anyway.
Find a way to make fitness fit in just the way your life is today.

Awareness Journal				
Date Time	Food and Fluids Type and Approximate Amt.	Physical Symptoms, Thoughts and Feelings	How Hungry Am I?	
			Before Eating	After Eating

Thoughts about Exercise	Physical Activity Notes: FITT

Food for Thought

Eating to deal with certain emotions is simply a way of coping.
Once you're aware of how your using food, you have an opportunity to
meet your needs in a more effective way.

Awareness Journal				
Date Time	Food and Fluids Type and Approximate Amt.	Physical Symptoms, Thoughts and Feelings	How Hungry Am I?	
			Before Eating	After Eating

Thoughts about Exercise	Physical Activity Notes: FITT

Food for Thought

*Start thinking of your self as an active, healthy person—
and you will become one!*

Awareness Journal				
Date Time	Food and Fluids Type and Approximate Amt.	Physical Symptoms, Thoughts and Feelings	How Hungry Am I?	
			Before Eating	After Eating

Thoughts about Exercise	Physical Activity Notes: FITT

Food for Thought

If you continually struggle with fatigue and lack of stamina, you may be living in a state of slight dehydration. Imagine being able to boost your energy level just by consuming enough fluid.

WORKSHOP NOTES

THINK: WHAT AM I REALLY HUNGRY FOR?

The last workshop focused on "I'm not hungry, now what?" Now we're going on "Little Voice Patrol" and take a closer look at triggers for eating and strategies for dealing with them. Don't be surprised if at first you want to eat anyway because eating is familiar and comfortable. Change is uncomfortable at first. Here are some strategies for getting through the necessary discomfort of change until the positive effects take over.

STRATEGIES: CREATING NEW HABITS

○ **Be a problem-solver.** Consider all of your choices and look for creative solutions.

○ **Direction, not perfection.** Don't get trapped into thinking you have to do it perfectly. Instead, make a step, any step, in the direction you want to move.

○ **Baby steps.** Recognize that reasonably-sized changes—even baby steps or micromovements, that you are willing to practice consistently will help you gradually rewire what feels good to you.

○ **Be realistic.** Ask yourself, "Where is the door most open for me at this moment?" In other words, what can you realistically see yourself doing?

○ **Pros and cons.** Consider the rewards and consequences of your options and think about the likely outcome of your decision.

○ **No right or wrong.** There are no good or bad choices—just what is most effective for you under the circumstances.

○ **Learn from your mistakes.** Every mistake brings you one step closer to being an expert. Just do the best you can.

○ **Practice, practice, practice.** Consistency and repetition are the keys to reducing the necessary discomfort of change.

THREE MAIN TYPES OF TRIGGERS

○ Physical Triggers

○ Environmental Triggers

○ Emotional Triggers

Physical Triggers: Feed the Need

Food can be calming, energizing and pleasurable so people sometimes eat food in response to physical needs. Certain foods even activate the pleasure centers in the brain and reduce awareness of physical pain, illness and fatigue. To decrease your eating in response to these triggers, you'll need to learn to substitute other activities that stimulate those same pleasure centers. Here are some of the most common physical triggers for overeating and strategies to help you deal with them.

Wet Your Appetite: Thirst

Many people feel like eating when they actually need water. Thirst is a physical sensation but food is an inefficient way to meet your body's need for fluids.

Strategies: Try drinking a glass of water before you eat. Review Eat: Drink and Be Merry for practical suggestions for dealing with this common trigger.

Running on Empty: Fatigue

Your little voice might say, "I'm so tired; I need a snack for a little pick-me-up." Although hunger sometimes causes a feeling of low energy, eating when you actually need to rest will only make you feel more tired because your body has to work to digest and store the unneeded food. In addition, recent studies have shown a link between poor sleep and weight gain.

Strategies: Take a break and rest when you need it. Get enough sleep to reduce your risk of overeating and weight gain and help you feel your best.

Mouth Watering: Salivation

Salivating is a normal physical response to the sight, the smell or thought of appetizing food. Since salivation occurs with or without hunger, it's not a reliable sign that your body needs food.

Strategies: Look for other physical signs of hunger besides salivation.

Chew on It: Urge to chew, crunch or suck

A desire to chew, crunch or suck is a physical urge but that doesn't mean your body needs food. For example, some people feel like eating crunchy food when they're angry.

Strategies: If the urge is strong, look for non-caloric ways to satisfy it such as chewing sugar-free gum or ice. Of course, using tobacco is not a healthy way to satisfy this urge.

A Spoonful of Sugar: Pain

Pain and physical discomfort are powerful triggers for some people. Certain foods cause the release of endorphins which have pain relieving properties. However, the effects are very short lived and overeating and weight gain often compound the problem, especially for conditions like arthritis and fibromyalgia.

Strategies: Depending on the source of the pain, gentle physical activity, relaxation techniques, massage, alternative therapies, medications and other pain management strategies can provide effective and sustainable relief. Talk to your doctor for advice.

That Time of the Month: Hormonal Cycles

Cyclical hormonal changes in women may cause them to eat a disproportionate number of calories and prefer certain foods (like chocolate and carbs) right before their menses. If you're on a diet and this kind of eating is against the rules, it leads to guilt and bingeing. It doesn't have to be like that anymore because you are in charge.

Strategies: Don't use PMS as an excuse to binge; you'll feel far better when you continue to use balance, variety and moderation to guide your eating. However, rather than trying to resist hormonal fluctuations, see what happens when you listen to them and allow your hunger and cravings to ebb and flow naturally. You'll probably notice that you want to eat less the following week so everything evens out.

Just What the Doctor Ordered: Medication Side Effects

Certain medications can cause increased appetite and/or weight gain as a side effect or a direct result of the way the medication works.

Strategies: Talk to your health care professional about your medications and ask if there are other kinds that won't cause increased appetite and weight gain. If you must be on a certain medicine for medical reasons, put a little extra effort into making healthier choices and being physically active.

It Must Be My Thyroid: Medical Conditions

Low thyroid (hypothyroidism), menopause, and other conditions can affect your weight.

Strategies: See your health care professional if you suspect there is an underlying medical cause. A word of caution though. As a physician, I have had countless patients who requested hormone testing to explain their weight gain but it was uncommon to find abnormalities that would completely solve the problem. The tests may be worth doing but I encourage you to continue to focus on making healthy lifestyle changes.

 Review the environmental triggers above then write down the triggers that affect you and strategies that you will use to help you deal with them more effectively.

Environmental Triggers: What Are Your Bells?

Remember Pavlov's Dogs? Pavlov rang a bell every time he fed the dogs so eventually they salivated when they heard the bell even when he didn't give them food. If you pair eating with an activity on a regular basis, eventually the activity itself triggers the urge to eat. Common environmental cues that trigger overeating include people, places, activities and events that you associate with eating. Be creative when coming up with strategies for dealing with these common triggers.

It's About Time: Mealtimes

Society programs you to follow a schedule and conditions you to eat certain foods and certain amounts at certain meals. It may be more convenient or necessary to eat meals at certain times. Perhaps you're also in the habit of eating a traditional "meal" including a main course, side dishes and even dessert or it doesn't "count."

Strategies: Though it is challenging to change the mealtime routine, you can adapt it to fit your own needs. Keep a healthy snack handy; if you're consistently tempted to snack right before a meal, move the mealtime up or eat differently the meal before.
And remember, you don't need to eat a whole meal if you're only a little hungry. Sometimes just a few bites are all you need. Begin to think of a "meal" as exactly the right amount and type of food for you at the time.

By the Clock: Eating on a Schedule

Many experts and diets promote scheduled eating "to prevent hunger" and fuel your metabolism. The experts assume that you'll lose control of your eating if you get hungry. But now you know that exactly the opposite occurs; you're more likely to eat in a satisfying way when you're hungry – as long as you aren't *too* hungry.

Strategies: Learn to pace yourself by observing your natural hunger patterns. Establish a consistent meal pattern that matches your hunger patterns. You'll probably notice you get hungry every 3-6 hours, depending on what and how much you ate last.

Danger Zone: High Risk Times

Many people have times of the day that are high risk for overeating. For example, you may experience a late afternoon energy slump or a tendency to munch when you come home from work to help you transition into your evening.

Strategies: Know when you're most at risk and develop an alternate strategy. For example, create a recharge or transition ritual to help you relax or unwind. Perhaps you could save a favorite magazine or book to read, call a friend or walk your dog instead.

Seasons of Reasons: Holidays and Weather

Many people eat more in colder weather or crave different types of foods in different seasons (winter stews, summer salads). Holidays can be especially difficult because of all the social ties to certain foods and certain people. In addition, many of the foods you eat during this time may seem "special" and therefore, harder to eat in sensible quantities.

Strategies: These occasions repeat themselves year after year so you know what to expect. Create a plan for dealing with your triggers and make it a point to really listen to your body instead of the external cues.

Special foods will be even more special when you eat them mindfully, focusing on the appearance and flavors of the food, the ambiance, the other people and the reason you are all together. Try tasting small amounts of the foods you really want, asking for recipes and taking foods home with you to eat when you are hungry. And don't forget, those holiday cookies will be back before you know it and you *can* make turkey and mashed potatoes in July if you want.

Early Bird Gets the Worm: Preventive Eating

Fear of being hungry when it isn't convenient can drive you to eat before you need fuel.

Strategies: You wouldn't put a coat on *before* you need it because it would make you feel uncomfortable. Eating is no different. Like a jacket, have food with you just in case but remember, you can't satisfy hunger ahead of time. Besides, you probably have enough energy stored to last you until it is more convenient to eat.

Sweet Temptations: Sight of Food

Overweight individuals are more likely to be "food suggestible." This means you might begin to salivate and think you're hungry when you see appetizing food.

Strategies: If you are not *sure* if you're hungry, go somewhere away from the food to focus on your physical state. If you're not hungry, it's still fine to appreciate the appearance and aroma of appetizing food without eating it. Just think of it as a feast for the eyes. Admire it and say, "That looks wonderful!" and walk away. It also helps to decrease your exposure to the sight and smell of food when you're not hungry. As examples, don't meet your friend at a coffee shop if the pastries always tempt you and keep water at your desk instead of going to the break room if there's usually food there.

Feeding Frenzy: Trigger Foods

Some foods seem to call your name. In the past you may have tried to resist these foods so when you finally gave in and ate them, you felt like you were out of control so you overate them.

Strategies: Remind yourself that you don't have to be in control because now you're in charge. Here are two different ways to deal with foods that triggered you in the past.

One way is to keep trigger foods away until you feel more in charge of your eating. Keep other foods on hand that you really enjoy so you won't feel deprived. Then when you crave a particular food that you're concerned about overeating, go to a restaurant or a store and buy one serving.

Another way to deal with trigger foods is to keep a small amount around at all times. Some people find they are less prone to bingeing on that food when they know it will always be there.

Eye Candy: Food Displays

Seeing displays of food like candy or nuts in dishes and tempting foods when you open your cabinet or refrigerator can trigger you to want them. Even if you weren't thinking of food before, your little voice will say, "Oh, I want some of that."

Strategies: Out of sight, out of mind. Don't use food as decorations or leave appetizing foods in plain view. If a co-worker keeps food out, politely ask them to put it in a drawer instead. At a party, socialize away from the food.

Food Sells: Advertising

Food is everywhere in television and magazines because marketers know how food suggestible many people are.

Strategies: Get yourself a glass of water during commercials, avoid watching programs that focus on food and skip quickly over the food ads and recipes. Break the habit of eating while watching television.

That's Entertainment: Social Events

Movies and popcorn, sports and hot dogs, dates and dinner – all of these are common social triggers for eating simply out of habit.

Strategies: Instead of making food the main event, focus on the movie, the game and the other people. If you are physically hungry, choose the healthiest alternative that will satisfy you or bring a healthier snack from home. If you would feel deprived if you didn't have the popcorn, buy the smallest bag (without extra butter) and savor every bite. Time

your dinner dates to match your natural hunger rhythms [...] whole experience, not just the food.

What's In Store: Grocery Shopping

There is marketing science behind grocery store layout, fo[...] designed to trigger impulse purchases.

Strategies: Don't shop when you're hungry and make a li[st...] just around the perimeter of the store where the produce, [dairy, bakery and butcher are] so you'll stick to the basics, venturing down the isles only for items on your list.

Cooks Spoil the Broth: Preparing Food

Just a few extra bites while you are preparing food can add up to a lot of extra calories and spoil your hunger for the meal.

Strategies: Avoid tasting food while you're cooking. If you need to taste to adjust seasonings, take only a small amount and be sure to notice whether you are less hungry afterward and eat accordingly at the meal. If you feel overly hungry while you're cooking, stop and eat your salad to take the edge off.

Full Serve: Serving Sizes

Research has shown that larger portion sizes and larger serving dishes trigger people to eat more.

Strategies: Use smaller plates and buy or divide your snacks into single serving bags. Don't keep the serving dishes on the table to decrease the temptation to "finish it off." Clean up the kitchen before taking a second helping. While you're at it, pack a serving for lunch the next day to remind yourself you can eat it again when you're hungry.

Location, Location, Location: Food Associations

If you eat in front of T.V., in bed or standing in the kitchen, you may have an urge to eat just from being in those places.

Strategies: You can make it a family rule to limit eating to one or two rooms in the house and try to eat only while sitting at a table. This will decrease triggers like T.V. and reading and help you focus on enjoying your food without distractions.

Not All There: Mindless Eating

Many people have a tendency to ignore or be distracted from their hunger signals, especially in social settings.

Strategies: Be a picky eater in social situations. Make your choices carefully then enjoy them thoroughly. More on this later.

On the Run: Eating in the Car

Eating while you're driving will distract you from the road and from enjoying your food. Additionally, your choices may be limited to fast foods and convenience markets.

Strategies: Try not to eat in your car and avoid eating while driving. If you have to be on the road for work or travel, pack a snack or lunch and park to eat.

Telephone Tag: Talking on the Phone

If you eat while you're on the phone, your body won't register satisfaction because your attention will be on the conversation. Besides it's rude!

Strategies: Don't eat while talking on the telephone. Period.

Dinner's on You: Dining Out

When you have a "special occasion mentality" you'll be more likely to order less healthy food and eat too much. You may also try to get your money's worth, especially at a buffet.

Strategies: Ask yourself what type of food you want to narrow your choices before you go to the restaurant or look at the menu. Decide which course is most important to you at that particular meal or that particular restaurant. Then remind yourself you can come back to the restaurant another time to try the foods you choose to skip this time.

Bigger is Better: Large Portions

Restaurants often serve overly large portions to make their customers feel they're getting value.

Strategies: Value quality over quantity. Is it well prepared? Attractive? Fresh? Healthy? Co-order and co-eat so you can enjoy great food in portions that don't leave you feeling stuffed. You could also choose to skip the appetizer, order a half-portion or request a kid's meal. Be prepared to wrap up the extra as soon as you feel satisfied or estimate how much you think you'll need and wrap up the rest even before you start eating. Remind yourself you'll get to enjoy that food again when you're hungry.

Out to Lunch: Business Entertaining

"Doing business," networking and business travel often includes lunch meetings and invitations to meet over food and/or drinks.

Strategies: If you need to meet over a meal, try to have healthy choices available and be mindful of what and how much you're ordering and eating during the meeting. When possible, make plans to do business socializing around activities where eating isn't the primary focus.

A Little of Everything: Grazing

At a buffet or social event, tasting "a little of everything" can add up to a lot.

Strategies: Be selective; if you attempt to taste everything, you'll end up too full. Take a look at all of your choices then take small samples of the most appealing foods. If the food doesn't taste as good as you expected, stop eating it.

Food Pushers: Eating Whatever is Offered

Beware of eating something just because someone offered it to you or handed you a sample. Your little voice might say, "It's rude to refuse food" or "You can't pass up free food."

Strategies: Be polite but firm when turning down food other people want you to eat. You are in charge. If you are concerned about hurting someone's feelings, ask for the recipe or ask for some to take some home to eat later when you're hungry.

Work On It: Eating at Work

At work people snack to alleviate stress, break up monotony or give themselves a treat, even when they aren't hungry. The break room is usually a minefield of trigger foods like donuts, cookies, and snack foods – particularly around the holidays.

Strategies: Make eating and working two distinct activities and avoid eating while working. You may decide you'll only eat what you bring so you'll be less tempted to eat whatever shows up at the office. And steer clear of that break room; tell yourself, "It's not my food."

Review the environmental triggers above then write down the triggers that affect you and strategies that you will use to help you deal with them more effectively.

Emotional Triggers: What's Eating You?

Emotions are also common triggers for overeating. It may not always be obvious when you're using food to cope with feelings. You may think you're overeating "just because it tastes good" or because you lack willpower. If you don't really know *why* you overeat, you may be using food to cope. The *why* becomes clear only when you begin to explore your feelings. Behind "I want food" might be "I want love," "I want attention," "I want comfort," "I want to rest," "I want someone to listen to me," or "I want to tell people how I really feel but I'm afraid they'll reject me."

Your eating may not be a response to deep-seated emotional issues, just a way of coping with the demands of daily life or an attempt to bring yourself back into balance. Here are common reasons people turn to food to temporarily comfort or distract themselves. Once you've identified the cues and emotions that trigger your urges to eat, you can find better ways to distract, comfort, calm and nurture yourself without turning to food.

Taste of the Good Life: Pleasure

Food often looks good, tastes good, smells good and feels good so it's a way to delight the senses anytime, day or night. However, the temporary pleasure is often followed by discomfort, regret and sometimes, weight gain.

Strategies: What, other than food, delights and pleases your senses? Friends? Sports? Flowers? Bath oil? Candles? Find ways to create pleasure for your self that don't involve food.

Just Desserts: Reward

You might eat to reward yourself for your accomplishments or to treat yourself for getting through a difficult day or situation.

Strategies: If you feel you deserve a reward, you do. Start a reward fund by putting a sum of money into the fund whenever you need a reward. At the end of the week, treat yourself to something special (besides food). If you feel you need a more immediate reward, turn on some music, treat yourself to a phone call with a friend, read your

favorite magazine or take a stretch break. Don't forget to tell yourself what a great job you did – even if no one else does.

The Way to a Man's Heart is Through His Stomach: Love

Food is often used to show love and affection. Mothers and Grandmothers cook for their families, husbands bring chocolate to their wives and couples gaze at each other over romantic dinners. Food and love have been intimately connected throughout history.

Strategies: You can enjoy connecting with people you love over food while still using hunger and fullness to guide you. Also recognize when you're pushing food on others as a way to express love. Look for other ways to give and receive affection, including attention, words, touching and non-food gifts.

Spice of Life: Boredom

Eating can be a way to pass the time, occupy your attention or put off starting a mundane or unpleasant task. Some people find themselves in front of the refrigerator when they're looking for something to do – or postponing something they need to do. Of course as soon as you stop eating, you become bored again so you eat again.

Strategies: When you're bored and need something to do, remind yourself eating is only one of literally thousands of options. Review the section on distraction in the last chapter for great strategies.

Too Much on Your Plate: Stress or Feeling Overwhelmed

Life places many demands on your energy and time, compounded by unrealistic expectations and a sense of urgency. When you feel stressed out or don't have the skills you need to cope with stress, it takes its toll both physically and emotionally. This has a direct effect on your ability to manage your weight if you overeat in response to stress or use stress as an excuse for not exercising. In addition, the hormones produced during stress actually accelerate the storage of fat. Since you cannot get rid of stress completely, it's important to learn to manage it, before it manages you.

Strategies: Respect your own personal strengths and limitations; sometimes reducing stress means learning to say no and doing less. Make a list and prioritize what needs to be done. Increase the time you allow to do things and reduce the number of obligations and complications in your life.

Keep things in perspective by asking yourself, "What difference will this make one week or even one year from now?" and "Is this really important to me?" Make a conscious decision to slow down and become completely aware and focused on the moment and on one task at a time. You'll be more efficient, more effective and more likely to notice life's little pleasures.

Create a self-care buffer zone to make yourself more resilient and able to bounce back more easily from the stresses and demands of daily life. Don't waste time on "pseudo-relaxation" like watching T.V.; instead use more effective stress relievers like exercise, meditation, relaxation techniques, having fun or connecting with friends and family. More on this in Workshop 8.

Starved for Attention: Loneliness

Food is a loyal companion that doesn't ask much from you in return. However it is a poor substitute for human interaction and relationships.

Strategies: Practice enjoying your own company by exploring your interests and working on your own personal development. Expand your circle by thinking about people who are in your life now that you could connect with. Think about where you could meet people; consider work, neighborhood, churches, hobbies, classes, and clubs. Most communities have numerous activities for all types of interests.

Chew On It: Worry and Tension

Feeling worried, nervous or tense is a normal part of everyday life but can trigger eating for some people because it can be distracting and soothing temporarily. However, if anxiety is frequent, persistent or severe and out of proportion to the seriousness or likelihood of the feared event, you may have an underlying anxiety disorder. See a health professional to discuss options for treatment.

Strategies: Worrying about the past or the future robs you of the present. Ask yourself "What can I realistically do to change the situation?" If there is a small step you can take then take it. If not, decide if you are willing to continue to give the thoughts your attention and energy. Worrying is often a habit and a habit takes awareness and effort to change. Professional assistance can help if you find yourself stuck.

Choke It Down: Sadness

Feeling disappointed, unhappy, gloomy, depressed, hopeless or grief-stricken may cause you to seek out food to comfort or distract you. Again, food cannot truly soothe your hurts and only distracts you temporarily. If sadness is persistent or disruptive, you may have depression. Trying to manage your weight when you have untreated depression can be an uphill battle. See your health professional.

Strategies: When you're experiencing sadness, soothe, encourage and comfort yourself the way a loving parent might respond to a child. Remember your feelings will ebb and flow and eventually dissipate but for now, try ways other than eating to comfort yourself. You may find it helpful to journal, talk, pray, meditate or just cry for awhile.

Sometimes people don't let themselves feel sad because they're afraid they'll fall into an emotional abyss or turn on an emotional faucet that will continue to leak through into the rest of the day or at inappropriate times. In order to manage these emotional remnants or unfinished business after you have dealt with your feelings it's helpful to create a "container" to put the remnants in until you can return to do more work on the issue. You can imagine yourself blowing your feelings into an imaginary bottle then corking it off until later or you can use a real container like an envelope or box to place your journaling in. Mentally or physically place your feelings into the container, then re-engage yourself into your daily activities fully and mindfully.

Can't Stomach the Thought: Avoidance

In avoidance eating, people eat to numb out emotional pain they feel unable to resolve. Using food for sedation is similar to using drugs or alcohol to avoid experiencing feelings. This can quickly take on an addictive quality and spiral into a pattern of abusing food. Sometimes people eat to stay in denial about an important issue that is painful to address, such as whether to leave an unhappy marriage. People who avoid confrontation and conflict may also stuff feelings, thoughts and opinions down with food rather than expressing themselves assertively.

Strategies: FEAST is very helpful for identifying what you're trying to avoid. However, be quick to ask for help from your physician, counselor or other trusted advisor if you're using food in an abusive manner. Take good care of yourself by seeking support and new skills when you need them.

Swallow Your Pride: Guilt and Shame

People sometimes overeat to punish themselves when they feel guilty or ashamed about their eating or about something else that happened, even in the distant past.

Strategies: Everybody makes mistakes and acknowledging your errors makes it possible to learn valuable lessons. When you're feeling guilty, ask yourself about your contribution to a particular situation. Ask yourself, "If I knew then what I know now and was operating at my best, what do I wish I would have done differently?" Rather than shaming yourself, this is an opportunity to accept appropriate responsibility, ask forgiveness, learn the lesson and move on.

Fed Up: Anger

Anger is a normal emotion that ranges from annoyed, irritated, frustrated, resentful, hostile, or infuriated to enraged. Some people have been taught that anger is bad and they shouldn't feel it or show it, so they use food to stuff or express it instead. Eating can be a way to turn the anger against themselves or punish someone else. However,

when people stuff anger, it often erupts even more fiercely at a later time, often in response to an unrelated or minor event, affirming their belief that anger is bad.

Strategies: Assure yourself anger is a healthy feeling that should be expressed in a healthy way. That might include telling someone how you feel, writing an angry letter you don't intend to send, screaming into a pillow or exerting yourself physically through exercise or a hobby like woodworking. After dealing with difficult emotions like anger, it helps to shift gears by focusing on something that inspires opposite feelings. For example, you could watch a funny movie or talk to a friend who always makes you happy.

Negative Feedback: Negative Self-Talk

Your thoughts are the primary creator of your emotions, which inspire your actions and lead to your results. Therefore, negative thinking leads to negative feelings and actions that create self-fulfilling outcomes. For example, when your little voice says, "I can't do that," you'll feel inadequate so you don't try at all and therefore, you prove that indeed, you can't do it. Your negative little voice may also serve up hypercritical messages to try to keep you "in line." However, people are not motivated by criticism – even when you are the one criticizing yourself. As a result, you probably won't do your best, which only proves your inner critic was right—and leads to more harsh criticism and feelings of inadequacy and hopelessness.

Strategies: The first step in developing a more positive internal dialogue is to begin to notice, without judgment, what you are thinking, how it impacts your feelings and your resulting behaviors. You will probably recognize much of your self-talk as inaccurate, ineffective, or limiting. Observing your thought patterns can provide you with important information about what drives the feelings that lead you to overeat.

Once you are aware, you can choose to change your self-talk by using the nurturing inner voice you use to speak to people you care about (especially children). It's gentle, reassuring, and understanding without being critical or judgmental. Practice using this kinder voice that leads to the feelings, behaviors and results you really want.

Not Good Enough: Perfectionistic Thinking

Expecting perfection from yourself or others guarantees you will never be satisfied. The frustration that results from "missing the mark" can lead to overeating. While it's important to do your best, perfection isn't possible or necessary. Constantly striving for it just chews up a lot of your time and energy.

Strategies: Ask yourself "What would be a more reasonable expectation of the situation or myself? What would be a more realistic and empowering way of talking to myself about this?" Be willing to make mistakes since these are an opportunity for learning and growth.

Body Language: Communicating with Body Size

Sometimes people eat (or don't eat) to communicate information to others with their body size. For example, a large body may be a way of telling other people that you are powerful and strong or that you don't want to be approached.

Strategies: Consider whether you eat to maintain a body size that says something to others around you. This is a fairly complicated issue and one that you may wish to explore with a counselor or therapist. The goal is to learn to communicate your needs, wants and boundaries in the most effective ways possible.

Soul Food: Spiritual Needs

When people have unmet spiritual needs they may experience a vague longing for something. They may be searching for meaning or purpose in their life but reach for food to fill the void instead.

Strategies: Prayer, meditation, worship and reading inspirational works will help you connect spiritually. Seek out a community or a guide to help you on your spiritual journey.

Slim Chance: Diet Mentality

Diet mentality is a powerful trigger for overeating. You may feel virtuous for eating foods associated with slimness and feel guilty for eating "bad" foods. Your little voice will say you should, shouldn't, must, ought, always and never. This usually backfires because when you don't do what you "should have," you feel guilty and rebellious. Be sure you haven't turned this into a diet too. In other words, don't beat yourself up when you eat even though you aren't hungry. Eating is a legitimate option when you are in charge.

Strategies: Develop a whole new relationship with food, one built not on guilt and shame but on satisfaction and health. Use words that indicate a choice such as "could, can, may, prefer and sometimes." For example, "I can choose to eat (fill in the blank) if I want it" or "I would prefer to eat a salad." "I will make healthy choices for myself, but I will make them because I want to, not because I have to."

Practice using hunger and satisfaction to guide when and how much you eat. You can make the best decisions for yourself no matter what the situation, instead of turning to a restrictive set of rules.

Forbidden Food: Deprivation

People who believe they must deprive themselves of certain foods will often become more sensitive to the sight and aroma of food, especially the foods that they deem "illegal." They develop powerful cravings and will often say they're "hungry all the time."

Strategies: Remember all foods fit. There are no "good" foods or "bad" foods when you're eating to satisfy physical hunger. Make healthy choices by considering the principles of balance, variety and moderation.

Dying to Be Thin: Eating Disorders

Eating disorders such as anorexia nervosa, bulimia and binge eating are important and treatable medical problems. Symptoms include starving yourself, bingeing, purging by forcing yourself to vomit, using laxatives or exercising excessively.

Strategies: If you experience symptoms of an eating disorder, seek help from your doctor or therapist.

Numbers Game: Weighing Yourself

Weighing yourself too often can lead to negative feelings that lead to overeating. People sometimes eat when they've gained weight but they also eat to celebrate weight loss. Weighing yourself often may also cause you to think about the external number on the scale rather than your own behaviors.

Strategies: You might find it more helpful to weigh just once a week or even just once a month. The rest of the time, focus on your behaviors and other internal signals to let you know whether you're developing new healthier habits.

Mirror, Mirror: Negative Body Image

The obsession with thinness in our society may have caused you to have distorted and irrational beliefs about your weight and your body. Body bashing and wearing clothes that make you feel uncomfortable can also lead to a negative body image, which in turn can lead to overeating.

Strategies: Remind yourself all bodies are okay, including yours. Wear clothes that make you feel comfortable and attractive and always focus your attention on your best attributes – and not just the physical ones.

When a craving doesn't come from hunger, eating will never satisfy it.

Your cravings can be a powerful source of information about your inner self and your true needs and wants. Remind yourself to think before you eat by putting a sign on your refrigerator that says, "What you're hungry for is NOT in here."

Review the emotional triggers above then write down the triggers that affect you and strategies that you will use to help you dealing with them in the future:

LIVE: ONE STEP AT A TIME

Cardiorespiratory exercise: Cardio = heart

Respiratory = lungs

Cardiorespiratory exercise increases your heart rate and causes you to breathe harder. Therefore, it strengthens your heart and increases oxygen in your tissues.

What types of activities are "cardiorespiratory?" Which ones interest you?

Examples of cardiorespiratory exercise include walking, jogging, biking, swimming, dancing, skating, aerobics, tennis, rowing, trampoline and soccer.

BENEFITS OF CARDIORESPIRATORY ACTIVITY

○ Conditions your heart, lungs, and vascular systems and lowers risk for heart disease
○ Lowers blood pressure and resting pulse, raises levels of HDL cholesterol (the good kind)
○ Increases stamina
○ Helps you lose excess body fat and tones your major muscles
○ Improves sense of well-being, improves sleep, boosts your energy level

GETTING STARTED

Walking is a great cardiorespiratory activity for most people because it is convenient, requires minimal equipment and can be easily adjusted for any level of fitness. What you need to know to get started:

○ Shoes – comfortable with thick, flexible soles.
○ Clothing – light, cotton; layer in the winter.
○ Sun protection – Sunscreen, hat, sunglasses.
○ Location – Anywhere! Look for an even surface.

- ○ Safety – Walk in safe, well-lit areas and wear reflective clothing at night. Let someone know where you are going and when you'll be back. Carry a cell phone.
- ○ Partners – can keep you motivated and interested. Kids and pets make good walking partners too.
- ○ Proper technique – keep your head level, shoulders back, stomach pulled in. Swing your arms down at your side or with your elbows bent to 90°.
- ○ Small steps – if you're just starting to exercise, take small steps toward your goal.
- ○ Break it up - if time is limited or you're just starting to exercise, spread your exercise throughout the day, such as 10 minutes 3 times a day or 15 minutes twice a day.
- ○ Keep it Interesting – doing different activities uses different muscles and skills and will help you stay interested. More variety means more benefits.
- ○ Pedometer – a pedometer is a step counter that you wear on your waist. It motivates you to be more active by showing you how quickly your extra movement adds up.

GET FITT

Frequency - Aim for most days of the week.

Intensity - Adjust to your fitness level. Increase intensity by moving your arms, walking uphill or pushing a stroller.

Time – 15-60 minutes depending on your fitness level. Choose a starting point on the sample walking schedule and increase your time gradually as your stamina increases.

- ○ Warm-up (5 minutes)
- ○ Brisk walk (5-60 minute)
- ○ Cool-down (5 minutes)

Type – See examples above.

Sample Walking Schedule:

WEEK	WARM-UP	BRISK WALK	COOL DOWN	TOTAL TIME	STRETCHING
1	5 min	5 min	5 min	15 min	After walk
2	5 min	7 min	5 min	17 min	After walk
3	5 min	10 min	5 min	20 min	After walk
4	5 min	12 min	5 min	22 min	After walk
5	5 min	15 min	5 min	25 min	After walk
6	5 min	18 min	5 min	28 min	After walk
7	5 min	21 min	5 min	31 min	After walk
8	5 min	24 min	5 min	34 min	After walk
9	5 min	27 min	5 min	37 min	After walk
10	5 min	30 min	5 min	40 min	After walk
11	5 min	33 min	5 min	43 min	After walk
12	5 min	35 min	5 min	45 min	After walk

USE YOUR PEDOMETER TO ADD STEPS TO YOUR DAY

Remember the pedometer from Workshop 2? It is a great way to measure and increase your lifestyle activity. It is also a great tool for starting a walking program to increase your cardiorespiratory fitness. (Copy the chart on page 97 to keep track long term).

 How many steps do you take on an average day? What lifestyle activities did you and will you add to increase your daily step count?

 What are your specific goals for increasing your cardiorespiratory fitness?

WRITE YOUR OWN FITTNESS PRESCRIPTION

Am I Hungry? FITTness Prescription

NAME_____ DATE_____

	Frequency	Intensity	Type	Time
❑ Cardiorespiratory:				
❑ Strength Training:				
❑ Flexibility:				

REFILL **FREQUENTLY!** SIGNED _____

TRACKING MY STEPS

Start Date _____ Starting average step count _____ I will increase by _____ steps each week

Step Count

	Monday	Tuesday	Wednesday	Thursday	Friday	Saturday	Sunday	A v e r a g e

EAT: CLEARING CARB CONFUSION

ROLE OF CARBOHYDRATES

Carbohydrates come from plants (or indirectly from plants in the case of dairy). The primary purpose of carbohydrates is to provide energy for your body to function. Carbohydrates are broken down into glucose molecules that float around in your blood stream (also know as blood sugar) and can be stored in the liver and muscles in glycogen packets that can be used for quick energy when your blood glucose level falls. The recommended intake is 45-65% of your total daily calories.

TWO TYPES OF CARBOHYDRATES

Simple Carbs

Simple carbohydrates are small packets of energy that can be digested quickly by your body so they may cause a sharp rise in your blood sugar (especially sucrose). They may give you a quick, short burst of energy that is sometimes followed by a rapid fall in blood sugar and energy. There are three kinds of simple carbohydrates:

Fructose - fruit, honey

Lactose - dairy

Sucrose - table sugar

Simple Carbohydrates: Review several days in your Journal. Using the following chart, "Simple Carbohydrates at a Glance," write the following letters next to the simple carbohydrates you ate:

F   Fruit

D   Dairy

S   Sugar

Now circle the simple carbohydrates you ate that contain fiber and write down the number of grams in the serving size you had.

Simple Carbohydrates at a Glance

Carbs	Sources	Examples	Typical Serving Sizes	Grams of Fiber
Fructose	Fruit	Apples, citrus, peaches	1 medium piece of fruit	3
		Banana,	or 1/2 cup chopped	2
		Berries	3-5	
		Melons, tropical fruit	1-2	
		Fruit juice	3/4 cup (6 oz.)	0-1
	Honey	Table honey	1 tablespoon	0
		Honey added to foods	Varies	
Lactose	Dairy	Milk	1 cup (8 oz.)	0
		Soft cheeses (i.e. cottage)	1/2 cup (4 oz.)	
		Hard cheeses (i.e. cheddar)	1 1/2 to 2 oz.	
		Yogurt	1 cup (8 oz.)	
		Ice cream	1/2 cup	
Sucrose	Sugar	Table sugar	1 teaspoon	0
		Corn syrup, table syrup	1 tablespoon	

Complex Carbs

Complex carbohydrates are long chains of glucose in the form of starch and fiber.

Starch – found in grain and grain products (bread, cereal, pasta, rice, tortillas), vegetables, legumes (beans)

Fiber – found with starches like grains, beans and vegetables and fruit. The fiber is removed from highly processed foods so look for "whole-grain" products.

❍ Fiber is indigestible so it is not broken down for energy.

❍ Fiber makes you feel fuller

❍ Fiber-containing foods cause a slower rise in blood sugar.

❍ Helps with digestion; helps keep you "regular".

❍ Recommended intake is about 25-30 grams/day

Complex Carbohydrates: Review several days in your Journal. Using the following chart, "Complex Carbohydrates at a Glance," write the following letters next to the complex carbohydrates you ate:

WG   Whole Grains
RG   Refined Grains
L   Legumes
V   Vegetables

Now circle the complex carbohydrates you ate that contain fiber and write down the number of grams in the serving size you had.

Complex Carbohydrates at a Glance

Carbs	Sources	Examples	Typical Serving Sizes	Grams of Fiber
Starch	Unrefined (Whole) Grains and Grain Products	Whole grains (i.e. brown or wild rice, barley)	1/2 cup	2-5
		Unrefined grain products Whole-wheat pasta	1/2 cup	2-5
		Bread, tortilla	1 slice, 1 6-inch tortilla	2-5
		Crackers	6 crackers	2-5
		Cereal	1 oz. (usually 3/4 cup)	3-7
	Refined (Processed) Grains	White rice, pasta	1/2 cup	1/2 -1
		White bread, tortillas	1 slice, 1 6-inch tortilla	1
		Cereals (refined)	1 oz. (often 3/4 cup)	1/2 -1
	Legumes	Beans, lentils	1/2 cup	5-7
		Nuts	1/3 cup	2
		Peanut butter	2 tablespoons	2
	High Starch Vegetables	Peas	1/2 cup	5
		Corn	1/2 cup	2
		Potatoes	1 small (with peel)	2
		Winter Squash	1/2 cup	6
	Low Starch Vegetables	Raw or cooked	1/2 cup chopped	1-3
		Leafy vegetables	1 cup	1
		Juice	3/4 cup (6 oz.)	0-1

GETTING THE MOST FROM CARBOHYDRATES

Balance

❍ Balance carbohydrates with other foods *and* balance the types of carbs you eat.

❍ Eating carbohydrates by themselves, like a piece of fruit, a few crackers, a slice of dry toast may satisfy hunger but it may not last very long. Eat carbs with protein-containing foods to keep you satisfied longer, so you eat less.

❍ Eating mostly simple sugars can lead to feeling hungrier, quick changes in your blood sugars which can affect your mood and your sense of well-being, cavities and in the case of sucrose (sugar), less nourishment.

❍ Eating enough fiber will make you feel more satisfied, level your blood sugars and increase your nourishment and health.

Variety

Instead of eating the same things everyday – like a bagel for breakfast, sandwich bread at lunch, apple for snack and a potato at dinner, eat a variety for more nutrients and more enjoyment.

Fruit

❍ Eat 2-3 servings a day. Your average _____

❍ Focus on color and variety to increase your nutrient intake.

❍ When possible, eat the peals and skins for more fiber and nutrients (wash first!)

❍ A piece of fruit is usually more satisfying and nourishing than juice because of fiber.

Dairy

❍ Consume 3 servings of dairy a day (milk, cheese and yogurt). Your average _____

❍ Choose low-fat and skim varieties; if you are currently using regular, you can change to low-fat slowly to adjust.

Grains

○ Eat at least 6 servings of grain or grain-products; at least 3 of these should be whole grain. Your average number of grains _____ Whole grains _____

○ Try whole wheat pastas, brown or wild rice and whole grain breads.

○ Try new grains: couscous, barley, quinoa.

Legumes (beans)

○ Excellent source of fiber, protein, vitamins and phytochemicals.

○ Great addition when going meatless – inexpensive and healthy.

Vegetables

○ Eat 3-5 servings of vegetables a day. Your average _____

○ High-starch vegetables like potatoes, corn and peas typically contain more fiber and more calories.

○ Go for color; vegetables with colorful flesh typically have more micronutrients.

Fiber

○ The goal for fiber intake is about 25-30 grams per day.

 Beginning with your morning meal, what choices could you make at each meal or snack that contain fiber?

Moderation

○ It is important to pay attention to your portion sizes of carbs and how they're prepared.

○ Pastas and potatoes loaded with cream sauce, butter or sour cream have a lot more calories and fat. See if there is a more healthful option like veggies or tomato sauce. The extras aren't off-limits; just use less and pay close attention to fullness since you'll probably feel full sooner when you eat them.

○ Moderation is also important when eating sugary foods since they don't provide other nutrients.

? Does your diet reflect balance, variety and moderation in your choice of carbohydrates? What are your specific plans regarding your carb intake this week?

PUTTING IT ALL TOGETHER

Fresh Fruit and Yogurt Parfait
Serves 1

Ingredients:
1 container of nonfat light yogurt with fruit (choose your favorite flavor)
½ cup of high fiber cereal
½ cup fresh fruit (strawberries, blueberries, raspberries, bananas)

Directions:
Layer yogurt, cereal and fruit in an attractive glass and serve for breakfast, snack, light meal or dessert.

Nutritional analysis per serving: (Varies slightly depending on brand of yogurt, cereal and choice of fruit). 162 Calories; 1g Fat; 10g Protein; 34g Carbohydrate; 9g Fiber; 2mg Cholesterol; 146mg Sodium.

Whole Wheat Pasta with Cherry Tomatoes
Serves 4

Ingredients:
4 servings of whole wheat pasta (tubes, bowtie, or angel hair all work well), prepared according to package directions.
1 pint cherry tomatoes
1 clove garlic, minced
1 teaspoon plus 1 tablespoon extra virgin olive oil
1 tablespoon balsamic vinegar
6 fresh basil leaves, washed

Directions:
1. While the pasta is cooking, cut each cherry tomato in half and sauté them in 1 tsp of olive oil for 4 minutes. Add 1 clove of minced garlic.
2. Drain pasta and return it to the pot.
3. Toss with tomatoes, 1 tablespoon of extra virgin olive oil, balsamic vinegar and basil.
4. Add fresh ground pepper and salt to taste.

Nutritional analysis per serving: 395 Calories; 5g Fat; 15g Protein; 79g Carbohydrate; 9g Fiber; 0mg Cholesterol; 8mg Sodium.

Salsa Fresca
Serves 4

Ingredients:
2 cups tomatoes, diced
1/4 cup onion, diced
2 tablespoons cilantro, chopped
1/2 jalapeño, finely diced
1 clove garlic, minced
1 tablespoon lime juice
1/2 teaspoon salt

Directions:
Combine all ingredients and refrigerate for 2 hours to let the flavors blend if possible.

Nutritional analysis per serving: 27 Calories; trace Fat; 1g Protein; 6g Carbohydrate; 1g Dietary Fiber; 0mg Cholesterol; 277mg Sodium.

Baked Tortilla Chips
Serves 4

Ingredients:
8 6-inch corn tortillas
2 teaspoons fresh lime juice (optional)
1 teaspoon chili powder (optional)
Vegetable spray
1 teaspoon salt

Directions:
Cut each tortilla into 8 wedges and arrange in a single layer on a cookie sheet. Sprinkle with lime juice and chili powder if desired. Spray lightly with vegetable spray and sprinkle with salt. Bake at 350°F until crisp and golden brown (watch closely!)

Nutritional analysis per serving: 114 Calories; 1g Fat; 3g Protein; 24g Carbohydrate; 3g Dietary Fiber; 0mg Cholesterol; 620mg Sodium

Crisp Pita Triangles: Substitute pita bread for tortillas in the recipe above. Season with paprika, herbs or garlic and serve with hummus or low-fat dips.

 Southwestern Soup
Serves 4

Ingredients:
6 cups vegetable, chicken or beef broth (use homemade or canned with no sodium)
1 medium onion, diced
1 16-ounce can of beans, drained (pinto, black, or kidney beans all work well)
1 16-ounce can of corn, undrained
½ tsp ground cumin
2 tsp chili powder
1 tsp garlic powder
1 medium zucchini and 1 medium yellow squash diced
1 16-ounce jar of chunky salsa (your choice of mild, medium or hot)
½ cup of instant brown rice

Directions:
1. Spray the bottom of a large pot with nonstick cooking spray and sauté the onion until it is translucent.
2. Add broth, beans, and corn and bring to a boil on medium high heat.
3. Add cumin, chili powder, zucchini, yellow squash, salsa and return to a boil.
4. Add instant rice and reduce heat to simmer.
5. Simmer for 30 minutes.

Nutritional analysis per serving: 336 Calories; 5g Fat; 19g Protein; 58g Carbohydrate; 10g Dietary Fiber; 0mg Cholesterol; 1012mg Sodium.

 Roasted Roots
Serves 6

Ingredients:
3 medium baking potatoes, peels left on, cut into ½" cubes
2 medium sweet potatoes, peels left on, cut into ½" cubes
2 yellow onions cut in eighths
½ pound of baby carrots
2 tablespoons olive oil
1 tablespoon dried parsley
1½ teaspoons kosher salt
½ teaspoon black pepper

Directions:
1. Pre-heat oven to 450°F.
2. Wash and cut up baking potatoes and place into a large plastic bag.
3. Trim any tough pieces off the sweet potatoes, cut up and add to the bag.
4. Place baby carrots in the bag.
5. Cut off each end of the onion then peel. Cut the onion in half then cut each half into quarters to make eight pieces. Place into the plastic bag.
6. Add olive oil, parsley, salt and pepper to the vegetables in the bag. Seal the bag and shake until all of the vegetables are coated.
7. Spread vegetables evenly onto a large cookie sheet and roast for 40-60 minutes, turning vegetables once or twice. Cook until vegetables are tender on the inside and potatoes are slightly crispy on the outside.

Nutritional analysis per serving: 163 Calories; 5g Fat; 3g Protein; 28g Carbohydrate; 4g Dietary Fiber; 0mg Cholesterol; 495mg Sodium.

 Toasted Angel Food Cake with Strawberries
Serves 6

Ingredients:
12 1-inch slices of store-bought angel food cake
1 pint of fresh strawberries, washed and hulled
6 tablespoons of light whipped cream

Directions:
1. Slice the strawberries and place in a bowl in the refrigerator until ready to use. Sweeten with artificial sweetener if needed.
2. Grill the slices of angel food cake over low heat for approximately 30 seconds on each side (until golden brown with light grill marks).
3. Lay one piece of toasted angel food cake on a dessert plate. Late a second piece so that it is overlapping.
4. Spoon sliced strawberries over the top and top with a spoonful of light whipped cream.

Nutritional analysis per serving: 292 Calories; 3g Fat (8.4% calories from fat); 7g Protein; 62g Carbohydrate; 1g Dietary Fiber; 8mg Cholesterol; 509mg Sodium.

ACTION PLAN

○ Set aside 15-30 minutes each day for reading, journaling and reflecting on this process.

○ Use Chapter 4 of your *Awareness Journal* to write down your observations and insights.

○ Identify your physical, environmental and emotional triggers and build strategies for dealing with them.

○ Start or increase your walking or other cardiorespiratory activity. Use the walking chart or a pedometer to help you.

○ Aim to eat 5 fruits and veggies, 3 low-fat dairy, and 6 grains (3 whole grains) each day. Eat whole grains in place of refined grains whenever possible. Eat sugary foods in moderation.

○ Gradually increase your fiber intake to 25-30 grams daily.

YOUR GOALS FOR THE WEEK

Awareness Journal				
Date Time	Food and Fluids Type and Approximate Amt.	Physical Symptoms, Thoughts and Feelings	How Hungry Am I?	
			Before Eating	After Eating

Physical Activities	FITT: Frequency, Intensity, Time, Type
Lifestyle	
Cardiorespiratory	
Flexibility	
Strength	

Food for Thought

Don't get trapped into thinking you have to do it perfectly. Instead, make a step, any step, in the direction you want to move.

Awareness Journal

Date Time	Food and Fluids Type and Approximate Amt.	Physical Symptoms, Thoughts and Feelings	How Hungry Am I?	
			Before Eating	After Eating

Lifestyle Activities	Physical Activity Notes: FITT
Lifestyle	
Cardiorespiratory	
Flexibility	
Strength	

Food for Thought

Recognize that reasonably-sized changes—even baby steps or micromovements, that you are willing to practice consistently will help you gradually rewire what feels good to you.

Awareness Journal				
Date Time	Food and Fluids Type and Approximate Amt.	Physical Symptoms, Thoughts and Feelings	How Hungry Am I?	
			Before Eating	After Eating

Physical Activities	FITT: Frequency, Intensity, Time, Type
Lifestyle	
Cardiorespiratory	
Flexibility	
Strength	

Food for Thought

Forget all or nothing. Become more active by starting wherever you are and increasing gradually, step by step.

		Awareness Journal			
Date **Time**	**Food and Fluids** Type and Approximate Amt.		**Physical Symptoms, Thoughts and Feelings**	**How Hungry Am I?**	
				Before Eating	After Eating

Physical Activities	**FITT: Frequency, Intensity, Time, Type**
Lifestyle	
Cardiorespiratory	
Flexibility	
Strength	

Food for Thought
There are no good or bad choices—
just what is most effective for you under the circumstances.

Awareness Journal

Date Time	Food and Fluids Type and Approximate Amt.	Physical Symptoms, Thoughts and Feelings	How Hungry Am I?	
			Before Eating	After Eating

Physical Activities	FITT: Frequency, Intensity, Time, Type
Lifestyle	
Cardiorespiratory	
Flexibility	
Strength	

Food for Thought

Cardiorespiratory activity provides you with numerous health benefits. Live longer, look better, and feel great—what's not to like about that?

	Awareness Journal			
Date	Food and Fluids	Physical Symptoms,	How Hungry Am I?	
Time	Type and Approximate Amt.	Thoughts and Feelings	Before Eating	After Eating

Physical Activities	FITT: Frequency, Intensity, Time, Type
Lifestyle	
Cardiorespiratory	
Flexibility	
Strength	

Food for Thought

Put a sign on your refrigerator that says,
"What you're hungry for is NOT in here."

Awareness Journal				
Date Time	Food and Fluids Type and Approximate Amt.	Physical Symptoms, Thoughts and Feelings	How Hungry Am I?	
			Before Eating	After Eating

Physical Activities	FITT: Frequency, Intensity, Time, Type
Lifestyle	
Cardiorespiratory	
Flexibility	
Strength	

Food for Thought

Sometimes, "I want food" really means, "I want love," "I want attention," "I want comfort," "I want to rest," or "I want someone to listen to me."

WORKSHOP NOTES

 THINK: WHAT DO I EAT?

Most programs focus on WHAT to eat. This is usually where you get your "list of rules". That's not the way it is with this program. Remember, there is only one "rule" – whenever you have the urge to eat, ask yourself, Am I hungry? When you're hungry, you can make the best possible choice for yourself. If you're not hungry, it doesn't matter as much what you choose since your body will store the excess calories anyway.

> Think about someone you know who eats instinctively. How do they decide what to eat?

Some people who eat instinctively are very aware and conscious of the food they select while others pay very little attention. The reason they maintain a healthy weight is that they follow their hunger and fullness cues rather than choosing a magical formula of certain foods.

There are three questions you can ask yourself to help answer the question *What Do I Eat?*

- What do I want?
- What do I need?
- What do I have?

What Will I Eat?

What do I want?

What? What do I need?

What do I have?

What Do I Want?

> Why is it important to ask yourself what you want first? Describe a situation when you didn't eat what you really wanted. What happened?

○ If you really want something, you'll eventually get around to eating it anyway. By then, you may be too full or feel too guilty to really enjoy it.

○ Denying what you truly want typically causes overeating in the long-run.

○ Satisfaction is not just physical fullness; it is also determined by whether you're enjoying the food you're eating.

○ Your body has "wisdom" about what it needs.

○ When you let go of "good food, bad food" thinking, certain foods lose their power over you so it becomes easier to tune into your body's wisdom about what it needs.

To figure out what you want, ask yourself:

○ Is there a specific taste, texture or temperature that I want?

○ Am I in the mood for a heavy or light meal?

○ Am I craving a specific nutrient like carbs or protein, or a specific food like pasta, salad, salmon, peanut butter?

What Do I Need?

Food decisions are not "good" or "bad" but clearly, some foods offer more nutritional benefits than others. As you consider what food to choose, ask yourself, "What does my body need?"

?   What types of things will help you decide what you need?

Balance, Variety and Moderation. What else have you eaten today? What are you likely to eat later? Have you used the principles of balance, variety and moderation to guide your eating that day or over the last several days? Your Awareness Journal helps.

Personal Health Inventory. Take an honest inventory of your health needs. Consider medical issues, allergies, family history, effects of certain foods on you.

? Take your personal health inventory. What specific issue do you need to consider when deciding what to eat?

Medical Issues (diabetes, high cholesterol, high blood pressure):

Goal is to lower LDL + raise HDL

Family history (diabetes, high cholesterol, high blood pressure):

Strong heart disease hx

Allergies:

Reactions to certain foods (do some foods disagree with you or make you lethargic?):

spicy foods = heartburn

Your health goals:

Lose weight so I might be able to go off the progestin + hence the Crestor.

Nutrition Education. Nutrition information is a tool, not a weapon. Use it to make an informed decision—not to punish and deprive yourself or make yourself feel guilty.

Healthful Alternatives. Ask yourself, "What is the healthiest choice I could make that won't leave me feeling deprived?"

What Do I Have?

What foods could you keep on hand to eat when you're hungry? Make a list of foods that you want to keep in your pantry, refrigerator, car and/or desk at work.

nuts, fruits, granola bars (healthy varieties)

Planning and preparation are critical for long-term success. Some ideas:

○ Keep healthy, appealing foods on hand like fruit, veggies, nuts, whole grain crackers, low fat cheese, yogurt etc.

○ Have healthy convenient/quick options available.

○ Bring a sack of groceries to work for the week. Have a variety of items that you typically enjoy for meals and snacks. When you're hungry, select what you're "in the mood" for. You'll feel more satisfied, make healthier choices and spend less money.

○ Plan meals ahead of time i.e. for the week or month and prepare a grocery list.

○ Keep basic cooking ingredients on hand.

Be Flexible

What you want and/or what you need may not be available. You have several options:

○ Wait to eat until you're able to choose what you want - *if* you're not *too* hungry.

○ Eat a small amount of food to tide you over until you can eat what you want.

○ Survey the choices on the menu or at the buffet then choose something that closely matches what you want and need. Ask for it prepared the way you want it.

○ Then listen carefully to your fullness cues so you don't overeat and promise yourself that you'll try to have what you really want the next time you're hungry.

BALANCE EATING FOR HEALTH WITH EATING FOR PLEASURE

? Describe your best day on a diet. What did you eat? Make a list of the meals and foods from breakfast on.

? Describe your worst day of overeating. What did you eat? Again, make a list of meals and foods from breakfast on.

Sour cream & onion potato chips — made me sick

? If you were going to create a day somewhere between these two extremes, a day where you ate healthfully but also ate foods you enjoyed, what would you eat from each of these days?

Can you imagine eating like this everyday for the rest of your life? That is balancing eating for health with eating for pleasure. Learning to balance what you need with what you want is one of the most important keys to this program.

Strategies: Nourish Yourself

○ Small, gradual changes make a big difference.

○ Try new foods, new recipes and use fresh ingredients.

○ Make it a habit to make the healthiest choice possible without feeling deprived.

Strategies: Get Rid of Guilt

? What are your "forbidden foods?"

Chocolate

ice cream

Here is a strategy for learning to eat those foods without bingeing.

- Choose one of your forbidden foods and give yourself permission to eat it when you really, really, really, really want it (The 4 Really Test).
- Buy or prepare a single serving or a reasonable portion or go out for it.
- When you really, really, really, really want that food, eat it mindfully without distractions.
- Notice whether it tastes as good as you imagined.
- If it does, promise yourself you can have it again when you want it.
- Be aware of your little voice. Thoughts like, "I shouldn't be doing this" or "I always binge when I eat this" will drive overeating and become a self-fulfilling prophecy.

Instead of a list of rules about what you can and cannot eat, you have three simple questions to guide you: what do I want, what do I need and what do I have?

Begin asking yourself these questions to make the best possible choices for yourself – and have fun balancing eating for health with eating for pleasure!

Stretching is a key part of a complete and balanced fitness program. Try this simple stretch break right now. Be gentle and listen to your bodies. Don't forget to breathe!

❍ Reach straight up over your head with both arms and really stretch (hold). Can you feel tightness in your back? Now relax. Does it feel better?

❍ Push shoulder blades together (hold). Relax.

❍ Drop your head forward and back carefully and only as far as comfortable (hold).

How do you feel? Isn't it amazing how a little stretching can make you feel so good!

BENEFITS AND PURPOSE OF STRETCHING

❍ Decreases stiffness and tension.

❍ Increases range of motion.

❍ Promotes blood flow and nutrient supply to tissues.

❍ Prepares your body for exercise and reduces muscle soreness after exercise.

❍ Improves posture and balance and prevents injury.

❍ Decreases risk of lower back pain.

❍ Makes you feel good!

? What specific benefits would you gain from increasing your flexibility?

Less chance of falling on the ice.

GETTING STARTED

❍ Warm-up before stretching (i.e. do not stretch cold muscles unless you are doing minor wake-up type stretches). A warm-up could be a 3-5 minute walk.

❍ Hold the stretch; don't bounce. Bouncing has a tighten-release effect that does not help lengthen the muscles. Try to hold each stretch for 20 seconds to relax the muscle completely.

○ Listen to your body. If something is tight, pulling or hurting, back off slightly until you're comfortable, then hold that position.

○ Take deep breaths during stretching. Breathe in then exhale slowly during the stretch. During the exhale, allow yourself to relax a little further into the stretch.

GET FITT

Frequency – 2-3 times per week.

Intensity – Stretching should be gentle and comfortable.

Time – Stretching can take 15 seconds to 20 minutes or more. Hold each stretch for 10 to 30 seconds.

Type – Stretch after exercise or stretch head to toe using the simple stretches on the following page. Try a stretch class, yoga, Pilates or a DVD.

WRITE YOUR OWN FITTNESS PRESCRIPTION

Am I Hungry? FITTness Prescription			
NAME_____ DATE_____			
	Frequency **Intensity** **Type** **Time**		
❑ Cardiorespiratory:			
❑ Strength Training:			
❑ Flexibility:			
REFILL **FREQUENTLY!** SIGNED _____			

FLEXIBILITY FROM HEAD TO TOE

Neck Stretch

Shoulder Stretch

Triceps Stretch

Lower Back Extension Stretch

Lower Back Flexion Stretch

Cat Stretch

Inner Thigh Stretch

Spinal Twist

Inner Thigh Stretch

Chest Stretch

Calf Stretch

Quadriceps Stretch

 **EAT: FAT FACTS**

ROLE OF FAT

○ Promotes normal growth and development (especially in children).

○ Maintains healthy hair and skin.

○ Helps absorb and transport certain vitamins (A, D, E, K).

○ Provides energy for the body (9 calories per gram).

○ Improves flavor and texture in food.

○ Increases satisfaction from eating.

TYPES OF FAT

Similar to carbohydrates, there are different types of fats, each with different effects on the body.

Saturated fats

○ Unhealthy fats

○ Generally solid at room temperature, such as butter, lard, fat on meat and poultry, cheese. In other words, fat from animal products.

○ Tropical oils are also saturated: coconut, palm, palm kernel oils.

○ Remember, **S**aturated fats are **S**olid at room temperature and **S**it in your arteries.

Unsaturated fats

○ Healthy fats.

○ Generally liquid at room temperature.

○ Two types: mono and poly

○ Remember mono unsaturated fats by "good COP": Canola, Olive and Peanut oil.

○ Polyunsaturated oils are other plant oils such as corn, safflower and sunflower.

○ Fish, nuts and avocado are also good sources of polyunsaturated fat.

Trans Fats

❍ Trans fats increase your cardiovascular risk and should be limited.

❍ Trans fats are formed when hydrogen is bubbled through liquid fats, causing them to form "trans-bonds," making them solid at room temperature.

❍ They are found mostly in snack foods and fried foods.

❍ Look for trans fat on the nutrition labels or look for "hydrogenated" or partially hydrogenated" oils in the ingredient list.

Review several days in your Journal. Using the chart on the following page, "Fats at a Glance," write the following letters next to the different types of fat you ate:

SF   Saturated Fat
PS   Polyunsaturated Fat
MF   Monounsaturated Fat
TF   Trans Fat

Add up your totals for each day then look at your average intake. Are the principles of balance, variety, and moderation reflected in your choices?

Do you plan to make any changes based on what you learned? If so, what are your specific goals?

FATS AT A GLANCE

Types	Structure	Examples	Role in Health
Saturated	All hydrogen atoms present Solid at room temperature	Animal sources: dairy, butter, meat, poultry, lard Plant sources: tropical oils like coconut oil, palm oil, palm kernel oil	Raises blood cholesterol (which increases the risk for heart disease)
Unsaturated - Poly - Mono	Some hydrogen atoms missing Poly = many hydrogen atoms missing Mono = one hydrogen atom missing Liquid at room temperature	Fish Fat found in plant-derived foods Poly: fish, vegetable oils (sunflower, safflower, corn, sesame, flax, soybean, cottonseed) Mono: avocado, olives, peanuts, oils: COP = canola, peanut, olive	Decreases blood cholesterol (which helps lower the risk for heart disease)
Trans	Made from unsaturated fats through a process called *hydrogenation* Liquid oils become solid as they are made to act like saturated fats	Margarine, shortening In the ingredient list, they are oils preceded by the word hydrogenated or partially hydrogenated Typically found in convenience and snack-type foods, candy, fried foods May be found in baked goods	Increased health risks

INTAKE RECOMMENDATION

○ Total fat: 20-35% of total daily calories.

Types of fat:

○ Saturated and trans fat: total 7-10% of total daily calories.

○ The lower intake levels are especially important for people at risk of heart disease.

○ Unsaturated: less than 10-25% of total daily calories.

GETTING THE MOST FROM FATS

Balance

○ Although the recommended intake for total fat is 20-35%, this does not mean that every meal and snack must be in this range. Instead, look at your total daily intake.

○ Balance is easier when you listen to your body. If you have a high fat meal, see if it takes longer to get hungry again. When you are hungry again, it's likely that you'll want something lighter.

○ With intake of fat, balance also means keeping your personal health needs in mind. To reduce risk factors for heart disease, choosing to eat beneficial fats the majority of the time is a wise choice, not a diet rule.

Variety

○ Fat is found in many of foods so strive to eat a variety of the healthful types and while limiting saturated and trans fats.

○ Olive oil is good for salad dressings and pasta while canola oil is better for baking.

○ Experiment with sources of beneficial fats found in fish, flax seed and nuts.

Moderation

Develop new habits to lower your overall fat intake and especially your intake of saturated and trans-fats. Ideas:

○ Try different new low-fat recipes and condiments (like mustard in place of mayo).

○ Order your dressing on the side and just dip the tines of your fork into the dressing instead of coating the whole salad.

○ Use tomato-based sauces rather than cream-based sauces.

○ Use olive oil based dressings in place of creamy dressings – and use less.

○ Choose baked snacks instead of fried.

○ Just remember, "low-fat" on the label doesn't necessarily mean low-calorie.

FAT: MAKING HEALTHIER CHOICES

A Healthier Choice:	Instead of:
Fats and Oils	
Soft tub margarine made with safflower, corn, or sunflower oil	Butter or stick margarine made with partially hydrogenated oil
Canola, olive, or peanut oil	Lard, shortening, meat fat, coconut or palm oil
Nonstick pans or cooking spray	Cooking with butter or oil
Flavored vinegar or salad dressing made with oil	Regular salad dressing made with tropical oils, cream, or cheese
Dressing and sauces on the side	Served generously over the top
Broth	Butter or Margarine
Mustard	Mayonnaise
Baked potato with low fat toppings	French Fries
Proteins	
Grilled, broiled, boiled, baked	Fried
Skinless chicken or turkey	Poultry with skin
White meat poultry	Dark meat
Lean beef trimmed of visible fat	Prime, heavily marbled cuts, or organ meats
Lean ground beef or turkey	Regular ground beef
Lean pork (loin, shoulder, leg)	Pork ribs or roast, hot dogs, bacon, sausage
Egg whites (2) or egg substitute	Whole Egg
Low fat varieties of fish	Shellfish
Meatless: beans, tofu	High fat protein sources

FAT: MAKING HEALTHIER CHOICES (CONTINUED)

A Healthier Choice: **Instead of:**

Breads, Grains and Cereals

A Healthier Choice:	Instead of:
Bread, Bagels, English muffins	Doughnuts, pastries, and croissants
Rice and pasta with low fat toppings	Fried rice, crispy noodles, cream/butter sauces
Low fat hot or cold cereals	Granola

Dairy Products

A Healthier Choice:	Instead of:
Skim or 1% milk	Whole milk
Evaporated skim milk	Cream or Half and half
Reduced or fat free sour cream, cream cheese, and yogurt	Regular sour cream, cream cheese, and yogurt
Low-fat cheeses (skim Mozzarella, cottage cheese or ricotta cheese)	American, Cheddar, Swiss, Brie and other high fat cheese
Frozen yogurt, ice milk, sherbet	Ice cream, shakes

Snacks and Desserts

A Healthier Choice:	Instead of:
Pretzels, light popcorn, flatbread Crackers, melba toast, nuts (in Moderation)	Chips, high fat or fried snack foods, crackers made with butter, cheese, partially hydrogenated oils (trans fats)
Angel food cake, graham crackers, fruit, gingersnaps, cookies, real fruit popsicles, sherbet	High fat cakes, cookies, candy, chocolate, desserts

PUTTING IT ALL TOGETHER

 Pesto
Serves 8

Ingredients:
2 cups fresh basil leaves
¼ cup olive oil
1 tablespoon fresh parmesan cheese
1 clove garlic
½ teaspoon salt

Directions:
1. Combine all ingredients in a blender until smooth.
2. Place in an airtight container and put a piece of plastic wrap directly on the pesto before putting the lid on to prevent discoloration. Chill until ready to use.
3. Use in pasta, on homemade pizzas, and on chicken or fish before grilling.

Nutritional analysis per serving: 64 Calories; 7g Fat; trace Protein; trace Carbohydrate; trace Dietary Fiber; trace Cholesterol; 129 mg Sodium.

 Grilled Salmon
Serves 4

Ingredients:
16 ounces of fresh salmon fillets
1 teaspoon olive oil
Salt and pepper to taste

Directions:
1. Pat salmon dry.
2. Rub with olive oil then season with salt and pepper.
3. Place on hot grill skin side up. Grill about three minutes then turn over and grill for another three minutes.
4. Top with Mango Salsa (recipe in Chapter 7).

Nutritional analysis per serving: 142 Calories; 5g Fat; 23g Protein; trace Carbohydrate; trace Fiber; 59mg Cholesterol; 556mg Sodium.

 Garden Salad with Cranberries and Almonds
Serves 6

Ingredients:
6 cups mixed greens
6 tablespoons dried cranberries (or substitute dried cherries or fresh strawberries)
6 tablespoons of sliced almonds

Directions:
1. Toss all ingredients together and cover with a moist paper towel until ready to serve.
2. Add Balsamic Vinaigrette just before serving (or serve dressing on the side).

Nutritional analysis per serving: 92 Calories; 5g Fat; 3g Protein; 11g Carbohydrate; 3g Fiber; 0mg Cholesterol; 15mg Sodium.

 Balsamic Vinaigrette
Serves 6

Ingredients:
1/2 cup olive oil
1/4 cup balsamic vinegar
1 clove garlic clove
1 packet non-nutritive (artificial) sweetener
Salt and pepper to taste

Directions:
1. Place all ingredients in a blender and blend for 30 seconds until emulsified.
2. Chill then pour over salad and toss.

Nutritional analysis per serving: 162 Calories; 18g Fat; trace Protein; 1g Carbohydrate; trace Fiber; 0mg Cholesterol; 1mg Sodium.

 ## ACTION PLAN

- ○ Set aside 15-30 minutes each day for reading, journaling and reflecting on this process.
- ○ Use Chapter 5 of your *Awareness Journal* to write down your observations and insights.
- ○ Ask the 3 "Whats?" to help determine what you are going to choose to eat.
- ○ Try the stretching exercises at least two times this week.
- ○ Discover new unsaturated fats that you enjoy; for example, balsamic vinaigrette made with canola oil, olive oil on bread in place of butter, grilled fish, etc.

YOUR GOALS FOR THE WEEK

Awareness Journal

Date Time	Food and Fluids Type and Approximate Amt.	Physical Symptoms, Thoughts and Feelings	How Hungry Am I?	
			Before Eating	After Eating

Physical Activities	FITT: Frequency, Intensity, Time, Type
Lifestyle	
Cardiorespiratory	
Flexibility	
Strength	

Food for Thought

Asking yourself "What do I want?" usually leads to greater satisfaction and more enjoyment—with less food. Remember the 4 Really Test!

Awareness Journal				
Date **Time**	**Food and Fluids** Type and Approximate Amt.	**Physical Symptoms, Thoughts and Feelings**	**How Hungry Am I?**	
			Before Eating	After Eating

Lifestyle Activities	Physical Activity Notes: FITT
Lifestyle	
Cardiorespiratory	
Flexibility	
Strength	

Food for Thought

Food decisions are not "good" or "bad." Some foods are "fun foods" while others offer more nutritional benefits. It all comes back to balance, variety, and moderation.

Awareness Journal

Date Time	Food and Fluids Type and Approximate Amt.	Physical Symptoms, Thoughts and Feelings	How Hungry Am I?	
			Before Eating	After Eating

Physical Activities	FITT: Frequency, Intensity, Time, Type
Lifestyle	
Cardiorespiratory	
Flexibility	
Strength	

Food for Thought

Remember that small changes really do make a difference. Healthy eating is simply the result of all the positive decisions you make.

Awareness Journal				
Date Time	Food and Fluids Type and Approximate Amt.	Physical Symptoms, Thoughts and Feelings	How Hungry Am I?	
			Before Eating	After Eating

Physical Activities	FITT: Frequency, Intensity, Time, Type
Lifestyle	
Cardiorespiratory	
Flexibility	
Strength	

Food for Thought

Taking a few minutes during a busy day to stretch and relieve tension in your muscles will reduce stress and help you relax.

Awareness Journal				
Date Time	Food and Fluids Type and Approximate Amt.	Physical Symptoms, Thoughts and Feelings	How Hungry Am I?	
			Before Eating	After Eating

Physical Activities	FITT: Frequency, Intensity, Time, Type
Lifestyle	
Cardiorespiratory	
Flexibility	
Strength	

Food for Thought

Keep a variety of foods on hand to eat when you're hungry that are satisfying but won't keep calling you, "Come eat me!" from their storage place.

Awareness Journal				
Date Time	Food and Fluids Type and Approximate Amt.	Physical Symptoms, Thoughts and Feelings	How Hungry Am I?	
			Before Eating	After Eating

Physical Activities	FITT: Frequency, Intensity, Time, Type
Lifestyle	
Cardiorespiratory	
Flexibility	
Strength	

Food for Thought

A few minutes of gentle stretching will relax your body and your mind.

Awareness Journal				
Date Time	Food and Fluids Type and Approximate Amt.	Physical Symptoms, Thoughts and Feelings	How Hungry Am I?	
			Before Eating	After Eating

Physical Activities	FITT: Frequency, Intensity, Time, Type
Lifestyle	
Cardiorespiratory	
Flexibility	
Strength	

Food for Thought

Balance your intake of higher fat foods with lower fat foods in the same meal or throughout the day to stay within the total daily fat guidelines for health and still enjoy flavorful foods.

WORKSHOP NOTES

THINK: HOW DO I EAT?

Close your eyes and remember one of your most memorable eating experiences. Think about where you were, who was there, what you talked about, what the ambiance was like, what the food looked and smelled like, how it tasted and how you felt.

 Now, pretend you're writing an article for a magazine. Write down as much detail about your dining experience as you can.

How often do you have eating experiences like you described above? How often would you like to have experiences like that?

Many people who struggle with their weight say they love food—but they usually don't eat in a way that shows they love food. They often eat very quickly, barely noticing what they're eating or they eat while distracted, watching TV, reading the newspaper, driving or working. This leads to mindless or unconscious eating because your brain can only pay full attention to one thing at a time.

What happens when you eat "mindlessly"?

Are you "mindless" in other areas of your life? What happens as a result?

MINDFUL EATING

Intention: Mindful eating is eating with *intention*. Be purposeful when you eat:

- Eat when you're truly hungry.
- Eat to meet your body's needs.
- Eat with the goal of feeling *better* when you're finished.

Attention: Mindful eating is eating with *attention*. Give your full attention to the activity of eating:

- Eliminate or minimize distractions.
- Tune into ambiance, flavors, smells, temperature and texture of the food.
- Listen to your body's cues of hunger and fullness.

BENEFITS OF MINDFUL EATING

- Increases your enjoyment of food and your pleasure and satisfaction from eating.
- Allows you to tune into your hunger and fullness cues so you're more likely to stop eating at a comfortable level instead of feeling stuffed and miserable.
- Helps you notice how certain foods and situations affect you.
- Gives eating less significance but more meaning.

STRATEGIES: MINDFUL EATING

Why and When?

- When you have an urge to eat, ask yourself, "Am I hungry?"
- Decide how full you want to be when you're finished eating.

What and How Much?

- When the answer is, "Yes, I am hungry," choose food that will satisfy your body and mind. Ask yourself:
  - What do I want?
  - What do I need?
  - What do I have?

○ Estimate how much food you'll need to eat for the level of fullness you're aiming for. Serve yourself only that amount of food.

○ If someone else has served your food, visually determine how much food you think you'll need and make a real or imaginary dividing line on your plate or move the rest into a to-go container.

How?

○ Create a pleasant environment. Set the table, put music on and maybe even light candles.

○ Minimize distractions. Don't watch TV, drive, work or read.

 What distracts you when you are eating?

○ Calm yourself before eating—and try to stay calm during your meal.

○ Sit down. Have only one or two rooms in your house that you eat.

○ Center yourself by taking a few deep breaths.

○ Look at your food. Appreciate the appearance, smell, colors and textures.

 Which food do you eat first and why?

○ Decide which food looks the most appetizing and take a few bites of that food first. If you save the best for last, you might eat it even if you're already full.

○ Put down your fork between bites rather than getting your next bite ready.

○ Stay connected and continue to enjoy the flavors, smells and textures.

○ Take small bites.

○ If the food doesn't taste as good as you thought it would, stop and choose something else if possible.

○ Pause in the middle of eating for at least 2 minutes and recheck your Hunger and Fullness level. Don't be surprised if you're already full at that point.

○ Notice when your taste buds become less sensitive.

○ When you feel satisfied, you're done. Push your plate away, cover it with a napkin or leave the table.

○ Remind yourself that you'll eat again when you're hungry.

○ When you're finished, check your Hunger and Fullness level again.

○ If you met your goal, congratulate yourself and remind yourself what you did to achieve this.

○ If you overate, analyze what happened; think about why you overate and what you can do differently next time. Most importantly, don't give into paralyzing feelings of guilt. We'll go into much more detail about this in the next workshop.

? Set aside time to walk through the strategies for Mindful Eating either by yourself or with a friend. Describe your experience:

Mindful Eating takes practice to become a habit. Eventually it will become second nature. Mindfulness is also an important concept that can be applied to all areas of your life. Use intention and attention in your relationships, work, leisure time, exercise—no matter what you're doing, to achieve optimal satisfaction from that experience.

LIVE: BE STRONG

Strength training or resistance training is any activity that requires a specific muscle group to work harder than it is used to. When repeated over time, those muscles will become stronger to handle the additional challenge.

 What are some examples of strength training activities?

- Lifting your own body weight (sit-ups or push-ups).
- Moving against the resistance of rubber tubing or a band.
- Lifting weights (including cans and jugs) or using exercise machines.
- Doing strength exercises using a stability ball which provides support and builds core strength.

BENEFITS OF STRENGTH TRAINING

- Improves your function in your daily life and decreases your risk of injury.
- Boosts your metabolism by building more muscle.
- Improves your body composition by increasing your muscle mass and decreasing your body fat.
- Helps minimize loss of muscle tissue while you're losing weight.
- Helps prevent age-related loss of muscle mass and strength.
- Improves glucose metabolism, blood pressure and cholesterol levels.
- Prevents osteoporosis by increasing bone mineral density.
- Decreases lower back pain by increasing core abdominal strength.

What specific benefits would you gain from increasing your strength?

GET FITT

Frequency - benefit occurs with strength training twice a week. Allow at least 48 hours before working a specific muscle group again.

Intensity - two to three sets of 8-20 repetitions for each exercise. If you can't do 8, the weight is too heavy; if you can do more than 20, the weight is too light.

Time - 20-30 minutes per session.

Type – See the illustrations on the next page and the examples listed above.

Strength training is not just for body builders; in fact most people don't have the time it would take to become highly muscled and women don't have the hormones to become bulky from working out. Strength training is really about increasing your muscle mass to boost your metabolism and function more fully in your life.

WRITE YOUR OWN FITTNESS PRESCRIPTION

Am I Hungry? FITTness Prescription

NAME_____ DATE_____

	Frequency	**Intensity**	**Type**	**Time**
❑ Cardiorespiratory:				
❑ Strength Training:				
❑ Flexibility:				

REFILL **FREQUENTLY!** SIGNED _____

SIMPLE STRENGTH FROM HEAD TO TOE

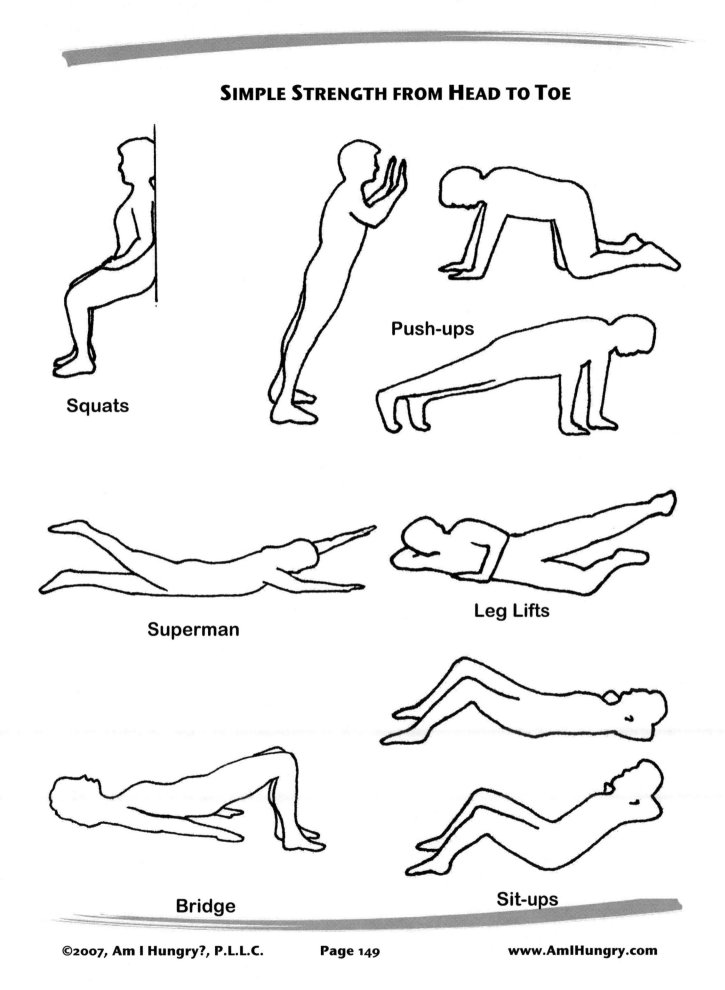

Squats

Push-ups

Superman

Leg Lifts

Bridge

Sit-ups

EAT: PROTEIN POWER

ROLE OF PROTEIN

○ Protein helps build, repair and maintain organ and muscle tissue. It is also important for production of enzymes and hormones, immune system function and fluid balance. It even helps maintain healthy skin and hair.

○ Protein can also be used for energy if necessary. One gram of protein is broken down to provide 4 calories of energy.

○ Eating protein helps you feel full longer.

PROTEIN BASICS

Amino acids are the "building blocks" of protein. There are 20 amino acids

○ 9 essential (must be eaten)

○ 11 nonessential (can be made by your body)

Like the letters of the alphabet, they can be arranged to make (or "spell out") the proteins needed by your body.

Types of Protein

Complete Protein: dietary sources of protein that provide all 20 amino acids. Which foods are complete proteins? Animal (meat, poultry, seafood, fish, eggs and dairy) and soy or soy products.

Incomplete Protein: dietary sources of protein that are missing one or more amino acids. Found in plant products (other than soy which is complete), for example, beans and grains.

Complementary Proteins: when these foods are combined, they provide all of the essential amino acids. Beans and rice are a good example. Complementary proteins do not have to be eaten at the same meal. Complementary proteins are especially important in vegetarian diets.

Protein at a Glance

Source	Type	Amount of Protein per Serving	Serving Size
Dairy	Milk	8 grams	1 cup (8 oz.)
	Soft cheese (cottage or ricotta)	14 grams	1/2 cup (4 oz.)
	Hard cheese	5-7 grams	1 1/2 -2 oz.
	Yogurt	6-8 grams	8 oz.
	Ice cream	3-5 grams	1/2 cup
Eggs	Egg	6 grams	1
	Egg white	3.5 grams	1
	Egg substitute	5-6 grams	1/4 cup
Legumes	Beans or lentils	6-8 grams	1/2 cup
Meat, Poultry, or Seafood	Cooked lean meat, poultry or fish	6-9 grams per ounce	2-3 oz.
Nuts	Assorted nuts	6 grams	1 oz., 1/3 cup
	Peanut butter	8 grams	2 tablespoons
Soy	Soy, cooked	14 grams	1/2 cup
	Tofu	10 grams	1/2 cup

GETTING THE MOST FROM PROTEIN

Balance

○ Too much of any one nutrient leads to boredom and can lead to nutrient deficiencies in the long-run.

○ Eating protein throughout the day at meals and snacks may give you greater satiety so you don't get hungry as often. You may eat less food and have more stable blood sugars.

○ A vegetarian diet may be a healthful, less expensive way of eating with the appropriate nutrition information.

Variety

○ Eating a variety of protein sources improves your intake of the amino acids your body needs, especially if you don't eat animal or soy sources regularly.

○ Protein containing foods also provide other nutrients, for example, dairy-calcium, beef-iron, pork-niacin. Eating a variety of protein sources provides a variety of nutrients.

Review several days in your Journal. Using the chart "Protein at a Glance," write the following letters next to the different sources of protein you ate:

D	Dairy
E	Eggs
L	Legumes
MPS	Meat, Poultry, Seafood
N	Nuts
S	Soy

Write down the number of grams of protein in the serving size you had of each. What are your primary sources of protein? What is your average daily protein intake?

Moderation

○ Because animal sources of protein may also contain saturated fat, choose lower fat types, trim visible fat, prepare them with as little additional fat as possible and eat reasonable sized portions for heart health.

○ Protein intake significantly above the general recommendation may have harmful affects on your body.

○ Your daily protein intake should be about 10%-35% of total daily calories.

? How much protein do you need each day? Calculate your personal average daily protein needs using the following formula:

<u>Your body weight (in lbs)</u>: _____ X 0.8 grams of protein = _____ grams of protein
     2.2 lbs per kilogram   per day   per day

Are you getting enough, or perhaps too much, protein? Eating an exact amount is not the goal but this calculation will help you assess your intake of protein.

? Are the principles of balance, variety, and moderation reflected in your choices?

? Based on what you learned from reviewing your journal, are there any changes you're going to make in your food selections?

? Do you, or are you willing to, "go meatless" sometimes? What ideas do you have for vegetarian meals?

PUTTING IT ALL TOGETHER

Chicken Fajitas
Serves 4

Ingredients:
1/2 cup unsweetened pineapple juice
1 tablespoon garlic powder
1 tablespoon red pepper flakes
2 tablespoons low sodium soy sauce
1 pound of boneless, skinless chicken breasts
½ red bell pepper
½ green bell pepper
½ onion

Directions:
1. Prepare the marinade by mixing the first four ingredients in a non-metallic bowl.
2. Cut chicken lengthwise into 1/4 inch strips.
3. Place the chicken in the marinade and cover. Marinate in the refrigerator for at least 8 hours or overnight. Drain the chicken to remove the marinade.
4. Cut peppers and onion into 1/4 inch slices.
5. Spray a non-stick frying pan with cooking spray and sauté the chicken, bell peppers and onion until cooked, approximately 8 minutes.

Nutritional analysis per serving: 177 Calories; 3g Fat; 27g Protein; 10g Carbohydrate; 1g Dietary Fiber; 69mg Cholesterol; 362mg Sodium.

Serving Suggestion: Wrap chicken and veggies in 6" whole wheat or corn tortillas and serve with homemade Salsa Fresca, shredded lettuce, diced tomatoes and Un-Refried Beans. This recipe is also great with lean beef, pork or shrimp.

Un-Refried Beans
Serves 4

Drain a 15-ounce can of pinto beans, reserving the liquid. Mash the beans with the back of a fork, adding liquid as needed to get a smooth consistency. Season as desired with lime juice, salsa, green chili or jalapeños.

Nutritional analysis per serving: 83 Calories; trace Fat; 5g Protein; 15g Carbohydrate; 4g Dietary Fiber; 0mg Cholesterol; 442mg Sodium.

 Brunch Oven Eggs
Serves 4

Ingredients:
8 eggs
½ cup light sour cream (not fat-free)
1 cup skim milk
½ cup shredded sharp cheddar cheese
4 green onions thinly sliced (white and green parts)
¼ teaspoon of salt and 1/8 teaspoon of pepper

Directions:
1. Heat oven to 325° and spray baking dish with non-stick spray.
2. Mix all ingredients and pour into the baking dish.
3. Bake 25-35 minutes until middle is set. Time will vary depending on baking dish.
4. Experiment with other ingredients such as mushrooms, peppers, green chilies, tomatoes, ham or other types of cheese.

Nutrition analysis per serving: 241 Calories; 15g Fat; 17g Protein; 9g Carbohydrate; 1g Fiber; 392mg Cholesterol; 710mg Sodium.

 Lettuce Wraps
Serves 4

Ingredients:
1 pound ground beef, extra lean

2 tablespoons each Hoisin sauce and peanut butter

1 cucumber and 2 carrots cut in matchstick sized pieces

2 tablespoons mint leaves

8 each Boston lettuce leaves

Directions:
1. Brown ground beef in large nonstick skillet over medium heat 8 to 10 minutes or until beef is no longer pink, breaking up into small crumbles. Drain thoroughly.
2. Stir in Hoisin sauce and peanut butter then heat through. Add cucumber, carrots and torn mint; toss gently. Serve beef mixture in lettuce leaves. Garnish with mint leaves.

Nutrition analysis per serving: 351 Calories; 24g Fat; 24g Protein; 9g Carbohydrate; 2g Dietary Fiber; 79mg Cholesterol; 250mg Sodium.

 ## ACTION PLAN

- ○ Use Chapter 6 of your *Awareness Journal* to write down your observations and insights.
- ○ Identify your eating habits that interfere with your ability to be mindful and decide what you'll do differently.
- ○ Practice Mindful Eating several times this week by walking through the strategy step by step.
- ○ Try strength training exercises two times this week.
- ○ Calculate your protein needs and compare this to your daily protein intake.
- ○ Notice how protein affects your Hunger and Fullness levels.
- ○ Add meatless meals to your diet a couple times a week.

YOUR GOALS FOR THE WEEK

Awareness Journal				
Date **Time**	**Food and Fluids** Type and Approximate Amt.	**Physical Symptoms, Thoughts and Feelings**	**How Hungry Am I?**	
			Before Eating	After Eating

Physical Activities	FITT: Frequency, Intensity, Time, Type
Lifestyle	
Cardiorespiratory	
Flexibility	
Strength	

Food for Thought

Choosing to eat "mindfully," in other words, eating with intention and attention, will give you optimal enjoyment and satisfaction from eating.

Awareness Journal				
Date Time	Food and Fluids Type and Approximate Amt.	Physical Symptoms, Thoughts and Feelings	How Hungry Am I?	
			Before Eating	After Eating
Lifestyle Activities		Physical Activity Notes: FITT		
Lifestyle				
Cardiorespiratory				
Flexibility				
Strength				

Food for Thought

When you pay attention to your body's signals and really savor your food, you'll feel satisfied with smaller quantities without feeling deprived. It is possible to truly enjoy food yet not eat to excess.

Awareness Journal				
Date Time	Food and Fluids Type and Approximate Amt.	Physical Symptoms, Thoughts and Feelings	How Hungry Am I?	
			Before Eating	After Eating

Physical Activities	FITT: Frequency, Intensity, Time, Type
Lifestyle	
Cardiorespiratory	
Flexibility	
Strength	

Food for Thought

Decide how full you want to be when you're finished eating. If you don't have a plan, you're more likely to eat more than you needed or wanted to.

Awareness Journal				
Date Time	Food and Fluids Type and Approximate Amt.	Physical Symptoms, Thoughts and Feelings	How Hungry Am I?	
			Before Eating	After Eating

Physical Activities	FITT: Frequency, Intensity, Time, Type
Lifestyle	
Cardiorespiratory	
Flexibility	
Strength	

Food for Thought

For a limited investment in time, strength training pays big rewards by increasing your metabolism and improving your muscular strength and endurance so you can function more fully in your life!

Awareness Journal

Date Time	Food and Fluids Type and Approximate Amt.	Physical Symptoms, Thoughts and Feelings	How Hungry Am I? Before Eating	After Eating

Physical Activities	FITT: Frequency, Intensity, Time, Type
Lifestyle	
Cardiorespiratory	
Flexibility	
Strength	

Food for Thought

Even when you are preparing food for yourself, make an effort to make it as attractive as if you were serving it to someone special—because you are!

Awareness Journal				
Date Time	Food and Fluids Type and Approximate Amt.	Physical Symptoms, Thoughts and Feelings	How Hungry Am I?	
			Before Eating	After Eating

Physical Activities	FITT: Frequency, Intensity, Time, Type
Lifestyle	
Cardiorespiratory	
Flexibility	
Strength	

Food for Thought

Eat without distractions so you can give food and your body's signals your full attention. If you love to eat, act like it!

Awareness Journal				
Date Time	Food and Fluids Type and Approximate Amt.	Physical Symptoms, Thoughts and Feelings	How Hungry Am I?	
			Before Eating	After Eating

Physical Activities	FITT: Frequency, Intensity, Time, Type
Lifestyle	
Cardiorespiratory	
Flexibility	
Strength	

Food for Thought

Becoming mindful will bring greater satisfaction and more pleasure to eating and all other aspects of your life—your relationships, your work, your leisure activities, even exercise.

WORKSHOP NOTES

THINK: HOW MUCH DO I NEED?

Think about what it means to be satisfied. Satisfied means that you simply don't need anything else – so you're left feeling content, fulfilled, pleased or even happy – just right. How wonderful to feel satisfied when you are done eating!

ENOUGH IS ENOUGH

Just as you use your Hunger and Fullness scale to let you know when to eat, you'll use it to let you know when you've had enough. Get in the habit of giving yourself a Hunger and Fullness number in the middle of eating, at the end of your meal and 20-30 minutes later.

Remember, the goal is to eat with intention. So before you start eating, decide how full you want to be at the end of eating then estimate how much food you'll need to eat to reach that level of fullness. Visually or physically divide the food on your plate. Then visually divide that amount in half and check in with yourself when you reach that point, then again after you are finished eating.

USING THE HUNGER AND FULLNESS SCALE

4 or less = Still a little bit hungry. Your options:

○ Wait awhile to see if your Hunger and Fullness number increases.

○ Eat more now.

○ Eat again in a while.

○ Stop at a 4; this is a good idea if you plan to have dessert, if you'll be eating again soon or when don't want to feel food in your stomach like before exercise.

5 = Satisfied - feels great! Remember this feeling.

- ○ I'm not hungry and I feel comfortable.
- ○ I don't feel the food in my body.
- ○ I could eat more but I don't need to.
- ○ The flavor of the food begins to fade.
- ○ Harder to give every bite my full attention.
- ○ I feel light and energetic and ready for my next activity.

How Much Do I Need?

Hunger and Fullness Scale

4 = Wait; I can eat more later

5 = Satisfied feels great!

6 = I am not uncomfortable

7 = I ate too much!

How Much?

6 = Full

- ○ I can feel the food but it is not unpleasant.
- ○ This is probably maintenance eating.

5 or 6 = Stop eating. Move away from the table, clear the food, clean the kitchen, cover your plate, package up leftovers.

7 to 10 = Very full to sick; "I ate too much."

- ○ Don't beat yourself up; use this as a learning opportunity.

? When you're in your Overeating Cycle, what typically happens when you overeat?

In an Overeating Cycle, most people just keep on overeating. But now, you're "in charge" of whether you choose to overeat so you're not good or bad. But you might feel physically good or bad—and therefore feel regretful. Don't "throw in the towel" and get trapped in guilt that fuels your Overeating Cycle. Instead, try to learn what you can from the experience. Notice how you feel both physically and emotionally. Try to remember all of the details so you can recall them the next time you're tempted to keep eating.

STRATEGIES: I ATE TOO MUCH!

Step 1: How do I feel?

? How do you feel when you've eaten too much?

○ Bloated

○ Stuffed

○ Nausea or queasiness

○ Short of breath

○ Sleepy, sluggish

○ Food didn't even taste as good at the end

○ In the past, guilty. However, since guilt only drives your Overeating Cycle, try to use the word "regretful" instead. There is no "bad" or "good" so no need for guilt!

Keep in mind that your stomach is only about the size of your fist so it only takes about a palm full of food fill it. Any more than that causes your stomach walls to stretch so your stomach gets bigger and takes up more room. That causes you to feel bloated and uncomfortable. Your body also has digest and process the extra food so that makes you feel sluggish.

I Ate Too Much!

Notice how I feel

Why did it happen?

What will I do differently?

When do I want to eat again?

What am I hungry for then?

How Much?

Step 2: Why did it happen?

Next, try to understand why it happened. Were you distracted, overly hungry, not hungry, eating for emotional reasons?

? Why do you eat too much? Make a list of all the reasons you can think of.

○ **Environmental triggers:** (sight and smell of food), social triggers such as eating out of obligation, eating food you paid for food or food that was free, keeping up with somebody else and other triggers.

○ **Emotional triggers**: All of the same emotions that trigger eating when you're not hungry can trigger eating past satisfaction. Ask yourself, "What was I thinking and feeling before and during this overeating episode? Is there some other need that I am trying to meet by using food?" When the underlying reasons are not obvious, they may be buried under denial or other coping methods. If overeating continues without any progress toward identifying and coping with your triggers, professional guidance may be useful.

Step 3: What will I do differently next time?

Make a plan for what you can do differently next time. After you've gathered your lessons from the experience, let the overeating episode go.

 Take a look at your list of reasons you eat too much. What could you do differently? Write down your ideas next to each reason.

Step 4: When do I want to eat again?

? Do people who eat instinctively ever overeat? If so, what do they do afterwards?

Even people who eat instinctively sometimes overeat. The difference is they usually don't feel guilty – but they may notice that they feel uncomfortable so they won't eat again for awhile. So if you overeat, just wait until you're truly hungry to eat again. It will take longer than usual to get hungry again and you may even decide you don't want your next snack or meal.

Step 5: What am I hungry for?

- ○ Don't punish yourself or try to compensate for overeating by restricting yourself.
- ○ Instead, ask yourself, "What do I want and what do I need?"
- ○ You're more likely to want something small or something light after eating a heavy meal.
- ○ You can re-enter your Instinctive Eating Cycle and compensate for occasional overeating by listening to your own body's wisdom and following the principles of Balance, Variety and Moderation.

The point of all of this is to feel better after eating—not worse. Keep reminding yourself that you're not going through this process to deprive yourself of food but to meet your physical and emotional needs more effectively.

 **LIVE: IN MOTION**

Have you increased your physical activity or are you still saying "I know I need to exercise BUT . . ."? It's time to take charge of your fitness to keep (or get!) yourself motivated so you'll stay in motion.

Attitude is Everything

Thoughts and feelings of obligation or drudgery won't lead to an effective and enjoyable physical activity. It's important to develop a new attitude toward exercise.

 What does your little voice saying about exercise? How can you change your self-talk to be more effective?

Go for Goal

Set SMART goals:

- Set **specific** goals and record your progress in a **measurable** way.
- Make sure your goals are small and **achievable**. When they are challenging but **realistic**, you can build a bridge rather than taking a giant leap across a canyon.
- Set a specific **time frame** for achieving the goal.
- Write your goal down as a **positive** statement. In other words, write down what you are going to start doing instead of what you are going to stop doing. This will give your brain a map to follow.
- Examples of SMART goals: I will play actively with my children every day. I will walk 2 miles 3 times a week. I will do full body stretches twice a week. I will do 25 sit-ups 3 times each week. I will take the stairs up to my office on the third floor at least twice a day.

 Write down at least three Fitness Goals for this week. Make sure they are challenging but realistic, specific and measurable, time-bound and written in positive language to give your brain a map to follow.

 What are your Fitness Goals for this month?

 What are your Fitness Goals for this year?

Reward Yourself

 How can you reward yourself for achieving your short and long-term goals?

Ideas for rewarding yourself:

- ❍ New music CD
- ❍ Movie
- ❍ Massage
- ❍ Pedicure
- ❍ New book
- ❍ Athletic clothing or shoes
- ❍ MP3 player to use while exercising

Get FITT

We have been using the FITT principle to get the most from your physical activity. We've talked a lot about Frequency, Time and Type so let's focus on Intensity.

Intensity: Target Heart Rate Zone

○ Your pulse is usually between 60-100 beats per minute.

○ To get the most benefits from aerobic exercise, exercise within your Target Heart Rate Zone (THR). This "challenges" your heart and lungs to work harder so they become stronger and more efficient.

 Practice checking your pulse, both at rest and with exercise. Calculate your Target Heart Rate Zone:

Estimated Maximal Heart Rate (MHR) = 220 – _____ (Your Age) = _____

Low end of your THR zone = 60% of MHR = 0.65 X _____ (MHR) = _____

High end of your THR zone = 85% of MHR = 0.90 X _____ (MHR) = _____

Intensity: Perceived Exertion Scale

The perceived exertion scale is similar to the Hunger and Fullness Scale. It encourages you to listen to your body.

> 1 or 2 – no or little exertion
>
> 3 to 5 – ideal range during active exercise
>
> Above 5 – very intense

The "talk test" can help determine your number on this scale. If you can comfortably hold a conversation, you're most likely between a 3 and 5. If you can sing, boost up the intensity; you're most likely only at a 1 or 2. If you're gasping for air and can barely utter a word, slow down. You are above a 5.

Check your heart rate or use the Perceived Exertion Scale regularly to monitor your intensity when you exercise.

 How can you increase the intensity of your fitness activities to obtain the maximal benefit?

Keep It Interesting

Boredom is one of the reasons people quit exercising.

 How can you keep your exercise interesting?

Some ideas for keeping your exercise interesting:

❍ Set goals and reward yourself for achieving your goals.

❍ Try new and different activities.

❍ Find an exercise partner (dogs and children on bikes or in a stroller count).

❍ Change location (walk in your neighborhood, at a local park, at the mall).

❍ Sign up for a fund-raising or competitive walk or run.

Your Top Priority — You!

The most common reason people don't exercise is a lack of time. But you have time for what is most important to you. Give exercise the time it deserves!

❍ Track your "time wasters" for several days, like watching a TV show you actually didn't really enjoy, playing a game on the computer, being inefficient, etc.

❍ Determine the best time of day for you to exercise. Many people find that morning is best because once it's done, it's done. Plus when you exercise in the morning, you'll have more energy the rest of the day. It may take time for you to get used to exercising in the morning so stick with it. Or, maybe evening is better for you. Ask your family to help you carve out 30-60 minutes 3-4 times each week to yourself.

○ Schedule exercise like an appointment in your day planner. If you have to cancel, reschedule just as you would any other important appointment.

○ Break your sessions into smaller increments if you need to.

○ Train your little voice to say positive things like, "I am an active healthy person and I live an active, healthy lifestyle." Your brain will automatically seek to make it true!

? Do you believe that exercise is important? If so, what are ways that you could make time for physical activity?

WRITE YOUR OWN FITTNESS PRESCRIPTION

Am I Hungry? FITTness Prescription

NAME_____ DATE_____

	Frequency	**Intensity**	**Type**	**Time**
❑ Cardiorespiratory:				
❑ Strength Training:				
❑ Flexibility:				

REFILL **FREQUENTLY!** SIGNED _____

EAT: NUTRITION AT A GLANCE

MICRONUTRIENTS

- "Micro" = small.
- Compared to the macronutrients (carbohydrates, fats and protein), these nutrients are needed in small amounts by the body.

TYPES

- Vitamins
- Minerals

Most people do not need to track their intake of specific vitamins and minerals. If you follow the principles of Balance, Variety and Moderation, your micronutrient intake is likely to be sufficient. Example of minerals that you may want to track more closely include:

- Calcium – 1000-1500 mg per day; found in high amounts in dairy foods; also found in broccoli, collard greens and salmon and sardines with bones. May also be added to foods like orange juice.
- Sodium – limit to 2400 mg per day (about a teaspoon).

GETTING THE MOST FROM MICRONUTRIENTS

Balance

- Different vitamins and minerals are found in different foods so eating a balanced diet will help you get what you need.
- One multivitamin and mineral tablet a day will help fill in the gaps.

Variety

- Variety is the key to consuming adequate micronutrients. No single food has them all.

❍ Take advantage of fresh fruits and vegetables in season (eat the skins and peels when possible – after washing of course. If fresh isn't available, frozen is second best, canned next (but watch the sodium in canned vegetables).

❍ Go for color. Vitamins and phytochemicals are found in greater concentrations in brightly colored fruits and vegetables.

❍ Go for nutritious "Power Foods," foods like blueberries, cantaloupe, mangoes, tomatoes and broccoli.

 Review your Awareness Journal. Do your choices include a variety of the foods that provide these important micronutrients? What specific changes will you make to help you get the most from your diet?

Moderation

Moderation is not a concern with most micronutrients unless you are taking supplements. In that case, don't exceed the daily recommendations.

NUTRITION LABELS

Use food labels to help you make decisions. Don't use food labels to classify food as good/bad or deprive yourself.

Take five to ten items out of your cupboard and refrigerator and take a close look at the food label. What nutrition claims and health claims do the labels make (like "heart healthy")? Are there any details explaining the claim?

Now, look at the Nutrition Facts. Look for the following information:

❍ Always start with serving size since all of the rest of the information is based on that quantity.

❍ Calories and calories from fat.

❍ Fat, including the breakdown of saturated, unsaturated and trans fat.

❍ Carbohydrate, including the breakdown of sugar and fiber.

❍ Vitamins and minerals.

❍ Use the following guidelines to help determine how well a specific food item provides specific nutrients (like iron and calcium).

> ❍ <10% DV = poor source
>
> ❍ 10-19% DV = good source
>
> ❍ >20% DV = excellent source

❍ Recommended Daily Values.

Now look at the ingredient list. They are listed in order from greatest to least amount.

 Last, look at the preparation instructions (if any). Are there ways that you could boost the nutrient content or lower the calorie content?

What did you learn about the foods you chose? Any surprises?

Based on what you learned, will you continue to use nutrition labels? Are you planning to make any changes in the foods you choose?

 **ACTION PLAN**

○ Use Chapter 7 of your *Awareness Journal* to write down your observations and insights.

○ Pay attention to Hunger and Fullness levels during and after eating. If you are above a 6, ask yourself why it happened and what you will do differently next time.

○ Decide what you need to do to keep your fitness plan interesting.

○ Set Fitness Goals for the week, the month and the year.

○ Develop a reward system for reaching your goals.

○ If lack of time has been an issue for you, track your "time wasters" this week and see if you can fit fitness in. You break it into small sessions if necessary.

○ Begin to read nutrition labels by choosing one or two things to focus on, for example, cholesterol, fiber or calcium.

○ If there is a particular nutrient you could improve on, identify at least three foods that are good sources of this nutrient that you will consume more regularly.

 **YOUR GOALS FOR THE WEEK**

Awareness Journal				
Date Time	Food and Fluids Type and Approximate Amt.	Physical Symptoms, Thoughts and Feelings	How Hungry Am I?	
			Before Eating	After Eating

Physical Activities	FITT: Frequency, Intensity, Time, Type
Lifestyle	
Cardiorespiratory	
Flexibility	
Strength	

Food for Thought

Think for a moment about what it means to be "satisfied"—you simply don't need anything else so you are left feeling contented, fulfilled, pleased, and even happy – just right!

Awareness Journal				
Date Time	Food and Fluids Type and Approximate Amt.	Physical Symptoms, Thoughts and Feelings	How Hungry Am I?	
			Before Eating	After Eating

Lifestyle Activities	Physical Activity Notes: FITT
Lifestyle	
Cardiorespiratory	
Flexibility	
Strength	

Food for Thought

The bottom line is that if you eat more than you need, you will feel unnecessarily uncomfortable and your body will have no choice but to store the excess fuel.

Awareness Journal				
Date Time	Food and Fluids Type and Approximate Amt.	Physical Symptoms, Thoughts and Feelings	How Hungry Am I?	
			Before Eating	After Eating

Physical Activities	FITT: Frequency, Intensity, Time, Type
Lifestyle	
Cardiorespiratory	
Flexibility	
Strength	

Food for Thought

Create powerful goals for all areas of your life – then write it down.

Your goals give your brain a clear map to follow.

Awareness Journal

Date / Time	Food and Fluids Type and Approximate Amt.	Physical Symptoms, Thoughts and Feelings	How Hungry Am I?	
			Before Eating	After Eating

Physical Activities	FITT: Frequency, Intensity, Time, Type
Lifestyle	
Cardiorespiratory	
Flexibility	
Strength	

Food for Thought

Before you overfill "your balloon," pause and take a deep breath.
Ask yourself, "Is it really worth feeling like I am going to pop or would I rather feel good when I am done eating?"

Awareness Journal

Date Time	Food and Fluids Type and Approximate Amt.	Physical Symptoms, Thoughts and Feelings	How Hungry Am I?	
			Before Eating	After Eating

Physical Activities	FITT: Frequency, Intensity, Time, Type
Lifestyle	
Cardiorespiratory	
Flexibility	
Strength	

Food for Thought

Regular physical activity is more important than just about anything you can do with your time and will make you even more productive in other areas of your life.

Awareness Journal				
Date **Time**	**Food and Fluids** Type and Approximate Amt.	**Physical Symptoms, Thoughts and Feelings**	**How Hungry Am I?** Before Eating	After Eating

Physical Activities	FITT: Frequency, Intensity, Time, Type
Lifestyle	
Cardiorespiratory	
Flexibility	
Strength	

Food for Thought

Reading nutrition labels is great way to learn more about the nutrient content of foods but they should not be misused to deprive yourself of certain foods or restrict yourself from certain ingredients.

Awareness Journal				
Date Time	Food and Fluids Type and Approximate Amt.	Physical Symptoms, Thoughts and Feelings	How Hungry Am I?	
			Before Eating	After Eating

Physical Activities	FITT: Frequency, Intensity, Time, Type
Lifestyle	
Cardiorespiratory	
Flexibility	
Strength	

Food for Thought

You don't need an excuse to have a wonderful meal—so why use a special occasion as an excuse to overeat? Besides, why would you want to feel uncomfortable if the occasion is so special?

WORKSHOP NOTES

THINK: WHERE DO I INVEST MY ENERGY?

Where you spend your energy is about much more than just exercise. It's about everything you chose to do. For example, in an Overeating Cycle your energy is spent on thinking about food, seeking, preparing and eating too much food. Your body stores the extra calories as body fat so you may have less energy overall. In a Restrictive Eating Cycle your energy is spent on diet and exercise, guilt and deprivation.

? Retake the Self-Awareness Quiz in Workshop 1 on page 11 (cover your original answers). What changes have you noticed? Do you have more time and energy on your hands when you're in your Instinctive Eating Cycle?

WHAT IS OPTIMAL HEALTH?

This program was designed to give you new weight management skills that free you up to spend your energy on building optimal health. Optimal health is the best state of physical, emotional, intellectual and spiritual wellness that you can have given your current limitations and opportunities.

○ Optimal health does not mean *perfect* health. For example, someone with cancer can have optimal health through good medical care, good self-care, a good support system, a positive attitude and a strong spiritual belief system.

○ No matter how hard you work in one area of your health, it won't provide the substance of another. In other words, no matter how much you achieve at work, it will not meet all of your emotional needs; no matter how fit you become, your physical health will not compensate for your spiritual needs.

○ When you care for all aspects of your health, you create a "self-care buffer zone" that helps you handle emotional and environmental eating triggers better.

FOUR ASPECTS OF OPTIMAL HEALTH

PHYSICAL HEALTH AND WELLNESS

Physical wellness is more than just nutrition & exercise. It also includes:

○ Basic bodily needs

○ Safety needs

○ Health needs

○ Nutrition needs

○ Fitness needs

○ Restoration (rest and sleep) needs

○ Physical/Sexual needs

? What can you do to invest in your physical health?

Investment Strategies: Physical Wellness

○ Establish a safe and secure physical space.

○ Take care of your health needs; get a check-up.

○ Eat fresh, healthful and interesting foods.

○ Engage in enjoyable physical activities and exercise.

○ Get rest and adequate sleep.

○ Give and receive physical affection.

○ Take a hot bath or long shower.

○ Get a massage, manicure, pedicure or facial.

○ Spend time in nature (walk, hike, camp, sit).

EMOTIONAL HEALTH AND WELLNESS

Emotional wellness doesn't mean always being happy. Emotional health is the result of learning to:

○ Embrace the full spectrum of emotions.

○ Identify and cope with stress and feelings.

○ Seek balance.

○ Learn to say "no" and know your limits.

○ Nurture yourself.

○ Cultivate healthy relationships.

  What can you do to invest in your emotional health?

Investment Strategies: Emotional Wellness

? What are ways of transferring emotional energy from the inside to the outside?

○ Release emotional energy by journaling, drawing, crying, screaming into a pillow or talking to a friend or advisor.

○ Spend quality time with family and friends.

○ Build intimacy with your significant other.

○ Practice effective communication.

○ Set appropriate boundaries assertively.

○ Read or listen to self-help and self-improvement material or attend other workshops like this one.

○ Do relaxation techniques and manage stress better.

❍ Practice forgiveness (with others and yourself).

❍ "Clean out the refrigerator" – deal with or let go of "old" stuff.

❍ Allow yourself to be vulnerable.

❍ Seek counseling or therapy if needed.

❍ Parent yourself more effectively. Others parented you when you were a child. Now you must parent yourself as an adult. Even if your own parents made mistakes, you can choose more effective ways of taking care of yourself.

? How does a "permissive" parent act and what are the results?

❍ They are indulgent, lenient, spoiling and/or inattentive.

❍ Results: The child may lack boundaries and doubt that he is really loved. May go through life expecting others to meet his needs.

? How does a "harsh" parent act and what are the results?

❍ They are overly strict and punishing. Love and acceptance are conditional on the child behaving as expected and being "perfect."

❍ Results: May be obedient initially but often becomes rebellious or people-pleasing.

In between these two parenting styles is the "firm but loving" parent.

❍ They set reasonable, clear boundaries but allow the child to make mistakes and will support and love them no matter what they do or what happens.

❍ Results: The child doesn't give up at the first sign of difficulty. The have a positive self-esteem, consider consequences of their actions and are willing to take risks in order to grow.

? How can you "parent" yourself more effectively?

INTELLECTUAL HEALTH AND WELLNESS

- Intellectual health is how you think, but also much more.
- Thoughts
- Growth
- Stimulation
- Creativity
- Challenge

? What can you do to invest in your intellectual health?

Investment Strategies: Intellectual Health

- Power of manifestation: your thoughts lead to your actions which lead to your feelings which lead to you behaviors which lead to your results.

  Thoughts > Feelings > Actions > Results

- Are your thoughts or self-talk:
  - Negative or Positive?
  - Powerless or Powerful?
  - Self-Defeating or Affirming?
  - Outdated or Forward Thinking?
  - Generalities or Specific?
  - Limiting or Growth Oriented
  - Problem Focused or Solution Focused?
  - Scarcity or Abundance?

Ask yourself:

- ○ What feelings do my thoughts cause?

- ○ What actions am I likely to take as a result of those feelings?

- ○ What results will I (or do I) get? Are those the results I want?

○ How are you stimulated intellectually – logical, structured and detailed? Or creative, abstract and random?

○ What types of accomplishments make you feel fulfilled?

○ What part of your brain do you most use in your daily life and job (logical or creative)?

What else can you do to stimulate your brain? Ideas:

- ○ Examine your priorities and set your goals.

- ○ Read interesting, challenging or classic works.

- ○ Learn something new: a new skill or language.

- ○ Do brain teasers and play challenging games.

- ○ Be creative: art, music, crafts and hobbies.

- ○ Visit museums or other novel places.

- ○ Take classes or study areas of interest.

- ○ Participate in stimulating discussion groups.

- ○ Explore occupational opportunities.

- ○ Travel or explore new areas.

SPIRITUAL HEALTH AND WELLNESS

Spiritual health may include religion, but it is really much more. It encompasses:

○ What "defines" you. Are you defined by your accomplishments and possessions, or by your character and personal attributes?

○ What determines your identity?

○ Sense of purpose or direction in life.

○ Knowing that there is something greater than yourself.

○ Connection and relationship with God.

o Connection with others.

o Unconditional love and acceptance.

o Contribution.

o Joy and peace.

? What can you do to invest in your spiritual health?

Strategies: Spiritual Health and Wellness

o Be fully present and practice mindfulness in all that you do.

o Pray, meditate and/or practice yoga.

o Spend time alone and quiet; seek solitude, connect with nature.

o Define your guiding principles.

o Write in a personal journal.

o Visit your place of worship (or find one).

o Read meaningful, inspirational works.

o Have an attitude of gratitude.

o Serve and contribute to others.

o Receive with grace.

o Practice kindness.

? What does it mean to have abundance – of food, money, time, energy, joy and love?

In terms of food, abundance means that there is plenty so you don't have to eat it all right now. When you use abundance thinking instead of scarcity thinking in other areas of your life, you're able to see all the possibilities. Since there is more than enough, the more you give, the more you receive.

Is any one of these areas (physical, emotional, intellectual or spiritual) calling for some attention in your life? Did one activity or another "speak" to you?

If you made a long mental "to-do" list, let it go. Strive for balance, variety and moderation, not just in the way you eat, but also in the way you live your life. Self-care is not about spending an equal amount of time or energy in each area. It is about making the commitment to care for yourself and meet your true needs.

Choose one or more ideas or strategies that inspired you. Create a short but specific Action Plan for putting that idea into motion. What *one thing will you do today* to bring balance into your life?

LIVE AND EAT: A FLEXIBLE APPROACH TO SELF-CARE

As you finish this program, you may be asking yourself, "What now?" You may even be a little concerned that you'll go back to your previous habits since that has probably happened after you went off some of your diets in the past.

But keep in mind, this isn't a diet. It's a new way of thinking that changes the way you eat and live. Here is another way of looking at what you've learned.

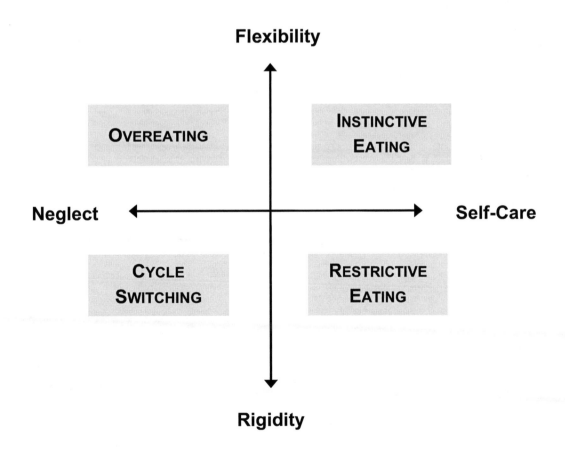

Now let's see what this means and how it can guide you for the best long term results.

Flexibility vs. Rigidity

On the vertical line, think about how you make your day to day decisions. At one end of the spectrum is flexibility. Flexibility allows you to adapt to any situation. Another way of thinking about flexibility is freedom, meaning that you can make any decision you want at any given time.

On the other end of the spectrum is rigidity. Rigid decision making is strict with no room for error or unexpected detours. When you try to follow a diet rigidly for example, you strive to be perfect without making any mistakes or ever going "off the plan."

Self-Care vs. Neglect

On the horizontal line, think about how the decisions you make affect your health and well being. At one end of the spectrum is self-care. Decisions that promote self-care will have the most desirable effects on your health. Obvious examples include exercising regularly and eating a healthy diet.

On the other end of the spectrum is neglect. You are neglecting yourself when your decisions ignore or disregard your best interests. Examples of neglect include eating high cholesterol foods frequently when you have a history of heart disease or eating too much before bed even though it gives you heart burn. In the extreme, neglect can even be abusive.

How Do You Make Decisions?

The flexibility or freedom to do whatever you want without regard to your best interests can lead to overeating and inactivity. On the other extreme, rigid adherence to a food or exercise plan may improve your health but comes at a high price.

Since it is nearly impossible to rigidly adhere to any plan that feels harsh or restrictive, you may shift back and forth between an Overeating and a Restrictive Eating Cycle.

Remember, we called that Cycle Switching. This neglects your physical *and* your emotional well-being and leads to guilt and shame, and ultimately, failure.

On the other hand, when you're eating instinctively, you strive to take good care of yourself while giving yourself the flexibility to adapt your eating and exercise patterns to fit your personal preferences and allow yourself to adjust to changing circumstances.

The Results of "Flexible Self-Care"

○ You listen again to your internal cues of hunger and satisfaction instead of trying to follow strict or arbitrary rules about your eating.

○ You build a strong foundation of nutrition information and choose from all foods freely to meet your needs instead of trying every fad diet that comes along.

○ You are physically active because it gives you energy, stress relief and an active metabolism instead of exercising to punish yourself or earn the right to eat.

○ You eat foods you really enjoy without guilt instead of depriving yourself or bingeing.

○ You eat mindfully in a manner that nourishes your body, mind and soul instead of eating unconsciously or obsessing over every bite of food.

○ You become aware of your thoughts, feelings and actions and how they affect you instead of judging yourself because you didn't follow a program rigidly.

○ You create a self-care buffer zone and meet your true needs instead of eating too much or neglecting yourself.

What To Do When You Get Off Track (and you will!)

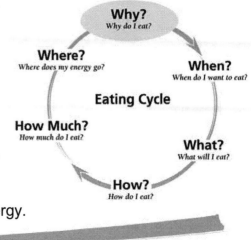

Unlike dieting, which may become more difficult over time, learning to eat instinctively again becomes easier with practice. Simply choose to use every opportunity to learn more about yourself and why, when, what, how and how much you eat – and where you invest your energy.

However, don't expect yourself to be perfect. It isn't possible – and it isn't necessary. You are in charge. Whenever you recognize that you are off track, notice which Decision Point you're at in your Eating Cycle and return to Instinctive Eating with the next decision you make.

How to use the Eating Cycle to get back on track:

Example #1 – In the middle of eating you notice that you are eating fast.

Why? You've been conscious about eating instinctively to meet your needs for nourishment and enjoyment. You are in an Instinctive Eating Cycle.
When? You were a "2" when you started eating.
What? You chose tasty, healthy food you wanted.
How? You are reading your mail while you eat. You realize that you've become distracted so you are no longer eating with intention or attention.

Back on Track: You decide to stop reading the mail until you're done eating. You slow down and focus on enjoying your food.

Example #2 – You find yourself overeating snacks and sweets all week at work.
Why? You had been losing weight gradually but you have a vacation to Hawaii next month. You decided to lose about ten pounds to look better in a bathing suit. You are back in a Restrictive Eating Cycle.
When? You try to eat only when you are hungry but after a week of dieting, you find yourself craving foods you thought you had stopped having problems with.
What? You were trying to avoid sugar and high-fat foods – but that seems to be all you think about.

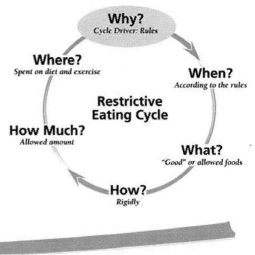

Back on Track: Clearly, trying to follow a rigid low-fat/no sugar diet has increased your desire for those foods. Instead of restricting yourself, you decide to increase your weight loss by focusing on **How Much?** by making sure that you eat to a "5" most of the time and **Where?** by adding more exercise. You cravings diminish almost immediately.

Example #3 – You notice that your clothes are getting tight again.

Why? You are in an Overeating Cycle and gaining weight.

When? You haven't been asking yourself, "Am I hungry?" because you know that most of the time the answer is "No" but you want to eat anyway. You guess that something is out of balance and driving your overeating, but until now you hadn't taken the time to think about it or do anything about it.

Back on Track: You commit yourself to asking yourself, "Am I Hungry?" whenever you want to eat. When you're not, you FEAST – Focus, Explore, Accept, Strategize and Take Action. It quickly becomes clear that you are stretched too thin and you have been rewarding yourself with food instead of taking care of yourself. You don't beat yourself up for gaining weight. Instead, you make a list of things you can do to nurture yourself – read an article from a favorite magazine, say a prayer, take a hot bath, ask for help or start to plan your next vacation. You begin to feel better and your desire to overeat decreases.

PUTTING IT ALL TOGETHER

You now have many new tools for your long term weight management (and life management) toolbox. Now you're in charge of using those tools to continue your journey toward instinctive weight management and optimal health.

ACTION PLAN

○ Use Chapter 8 of your *Awareness Journal* to write down your observations and insights.

○ Write your *own* personal inspirational messages in each of the "Food for Thought" areas of your Awareness Journal pages.

○ Chose one or two specific strategies for improving your physical, emotional, intellectual and/or spiritual health and wellness.

○ Take the time to set your priorities and decide where you'll spend your energy this week.

○ Don't expect yourself to be perfect. Stay aware and use your mistakes as learning opportunities by examining each Decision Point in your Eating Cycle.

○ Continue to practice your new skills until they become second nature. Remember that this is a process, not a destination.

YOUR GOALS FOR THE WEEK

Awareness Journal			
Date Time	Where do I invest my energy?	P=Physical I=Intellectual E=Emotional S=Spiritual	Notes and Observations

Physical Activities	FITT: Frequency, Intensity, Time, Type
Lifestyle	
Cardiorespiratory	
Flexibility	
Strength	

Food for Thought

Awareness Journal			
Date Time	Where do I invest my energy?	P=Physical I=Intellectual E=Emotional S=Spiritual	Notes and Observations

Physical Activities	FITT: Frequency, Intensity, Time, Type
Lifestyle	
Cardiorespiratory	
Flexibility	
Strength	

Food for Thought

Awareness Journal			
Date Time	Where do I invest my energy?	P=Physical I=Intellectual E=Emotional S=Spiritual	Notes and Observations

Physical Activities	FITT: Frequency, Intensity, Time, Type
Lifestyle	
Cardiorespiratory	
Flexibility	
Strength	

Food for Thought

Awareness Journal			
Date Time	Where do I invest my energy?	P=Physical I=Intellectual E=Emotional S=Spiritual	Notes and Observations

Physical Activities	FITT: Frequency, Intensity, Time, Type
Lifestyle	
Cardiorespiratory	
Flexibility	
Strength	

Food for Thought

Awareness Journal			
Date Time	Where do I invest my energy?	P=Physical I=Intellectual E=Emotional S=Spiritual	Notes and Observations

Physical Activities	FITT: Frequency, Intensity, Time, Type
Lifestyle	
Cardiorespiratory	
Flexibility	
Strength	

Food for Thought

Awareness Journal			
Date Time	Where do I invest my energy?	P=Physical I=Intellectual E=Emotional S=Spiritual	Notes and Observations

Physical Activities	FITT: Frequency, Intensity, Time, Type
Lifestyle	
Cardiorespiratory	
Flexibility	
Strength	
Food for Thought	

Awareness Journal			
Date Time	Where do I invest my energy?	P=Physical I=Intellectual E=Emotional S=Spiritual	Notes and Observations

Physical Activities	FITT: Frequency, Intensity, Time, Type
Lifestyle	
Cardiorespiratory	
Flexibility	
Strength	
Food for Thought	

Page 207   www.AmIHungry.com

CLASSMATES' CONTACT INFORMATION